METAL
CORROSION
IN BOATS

Second Edition

METAL CORROSION IN BOATS

The prevention of metal corrosion in hulls, engines, rigging and fittings

Nigel Warren

Adlard Coles Nautical
LONDON

Second edition published by Adlard Coles Nautical 1998
an imprint of A & C Black (Publishers) Ltd
35 Bedford Row, London WC1R 4JH

Copyright © Nigel Warren 1980, 1998

First published in Great Britain in hardback by Stanford
Maritime Ltd in 1980
Reprinted in paperback by Adlard Coles Ltd 1986
Second edition published by Adlard Coles Nautical 1998

ISBN 0–7136–4869–4

A CIP catalogue record for this book is available from the
British Library.

Printed and bound in Great Britain by
The Cromwell Press.

To
*Ray T for his friendship
and Janet who has brought
this unique book back to life*

Contents

coatings—Chinese or Swedish galvanizing—Tin, lead, nickel and chromium coatings—Nylon dipping—Sheathing with fibreglass—Cladding—In fresh waters—To conclude

Lead and solder—Uranium—Titanium—Magnesium alloys

Types of Corrosion

General wastage—Pitting—Velocity effects: impingement and cavitation

The galvanic series—Insulation—Fastenings—Nail-sickness—Antifoulings—Conclusion

Bonding to earth—Selective corrosion—Stress corrosion cracking—Hydrogen embrittlement—Corrosion fatigue—Fatigue-conducive conditions

Control and Prevention

Sacrificial anodes—Fibreglass and wooden hulls—Outboards and outdrives—Impressed current systems—Snags to cathodic protection

Keels and keel bolts—Lead keels—Choice of keel bolt material—Internal ballast—Sterngear—Propeller shafts—Propellers—Sterntubes and shaft struts—Seacocks—Rudders and rudder pintles—Centreboards—Fastenings—Outdrives and outboards—Antifoulings

CONTENTS

Tables

Introduction and Acknowledgements

A Black Art: that's how metal corrosion and its prevention is regarded by most boat owners and indeed by many boat builders. It is a subject not often presented in yachting magazines, or if it is, the author is a corrosion engineer and baffles everyone with science. This book is an attempt to fill the gap and be of use to boat builder and owner alike.

It is very useful for an owner to have a broad knowledge of the corrosion behaviour of the common boatbuilding metals and to know in what conditions they are likely to corrode too rapidly for comfort. In some instances it is vital to the safety of the boat: seacocks, for example. Such knowledge is also very useful when choosing new fittings over the chandler's counter because so often chandlery staff are quite ignorant. The effect of one metal on another when immersed in seawater is a particular aspect that is very important; fortunately it is easily understood and without a knowledge of mathematics or even science!

While there are broad theories that help to determine a particular metal for a particular purpose, its actual corrosion behaviour can be very variable because corrosion depends upon so many factors. Consequently hard and fast rules are very difficult to make. The natural tendency of any metal is to return to its original state in the earth, as an ore, and only good choice and subsequent maintenance can reduce the speed of this process.

Choosing more corrosion resistant and more expensive metals in the first place usually pays handsomely later on. A cheap brass domestic gate valve used as a seacock on a seagoing boat will surely give trouble after a few years. It may even sink the boat. Spend a few more pounds on a bronze one in the first place and its life will be long. This policy can be applied in all sorts of cases and even to the hull itself.

Of course, in the preparation of a book of this sort a great many technical sources have had to be consulted and these sources and their authors are hereby acknowledged. On the practical side, apart from experience on my own boats and in the course of my work as a naval architect, I would like to acknowledge the many and varied views and problems aired over the years in the magazine *Practical Boat Owner*, mostly by readers, that I have made use of here – subjects ranging from steel hulls to centreboard pivot bolts.

The Metals Themselves

Elements and their Symbols

Aluminium	Al
Antimony	Sb
Arsenic	As
Cadmium	Cd
Carbon	C
Chlorine	Cl
Chromium	Cr
Cobalt	Co
Columbium (Niobium)	Cb
Copper	Cu
Hydrogen	H
Iron	Fe
Lead	Pb
Magnesium	Mg
Manganese	Mn
Mercury	Hg
Molybdenum	Mo
Nickel	Ni
Niobium	Nb
Nitrogen	N
Oxygen	O
Phosphorous	P
Potassium	K
Selenium	Se
Silicon	Si
Silver	Ag
Sulphur	S
Tantalum	Ta
Tin	Sn
Titanium	Ti
Zinc	Zn

Chapter 1
Stainless Steels

Stainless steel is a relative newcomer to the boating scene. Its availability and use on boats coincided roughly with the mass change to fibreglass (GRP). Nowadays it is highly regarded and more or less a standard material for all manner of fittings and fasteners. Pulpits and stanchions can be fabricated from tube, stainless wire rope is very much the modern standard, while stainless bolts and screws are readily available. Even bollards and cleats can be obtained cast in stainless steel. The attraction lies in its bright, shiny, non-tarnishing appearance. It is also strong – stronger than many copper-based materials. And basically it ought to be cheaper than brass or bronze because most of its content is cheap iron (Fe).

Stainless steel owes its corrosion resistance to its chromium content. The type of stainless steel that is of most interest is basically an alloy of iron, chromium and nickel. Chromium (Cr) as a metal reacts with oxygen very rapidly to form an oxide film which is very tough and impervious to further attack. This property is conferred to the alloy of iron and chromium. As the amount of chromium exceeds 12% the corrosion resistance becomes very marked and rusting ceases to be a problem.

Thus the hard tough skin on the surface of stainless steel – due entirely to the chromium content – is the main reason why this metal has become so popular. The skin thickens and hardens when polished and rubbed.

The nickel content of stainless steel improves its resistance to acids. If sufficient nickel (Ni) is present it allows a particular type of crystal structure to form which in turn eliminates the need for any pre-heat or post-heat treatment when welding.

THE METALS THEMSELVES

There are of course many different types of stainless steel depending mainly on how much chromium and how much nickel is added. There are three main groups, namely austenitic, ferritic and martensitic. These names refer to the type of crystal structure of the resulting alloy. (The term 'alloy' means a mix of different metals and is not particularly connected with any one metal such as aluminium.) For marine purposes it is the austenitic types of stainless steel that are of most interest. The percentages of chromium and nickel that automatically create an austenitic stainless steel at room temperatures are shown in (1). Since nickel is the most expensive alloying metal, the most commonly used austenitic stainless steel contains 8% nickel and 18% chromium: the very bottom of the austenitic curve. This type is often called simply 18/8. It can be regarded as the lowest form of specification for a stainless steel intended for seagoing equipment.

In passing, it may be of interest to mention some of the wide range of stainless steels other than the 'marine' grades. The world-wide use of stainless steel began after the accidental discovery in 1913 that if chromium is added to iron it stops rusting taking place. A common group of stainless steels are those with about 12–14% chromium but no nickel. Table cutlery and turbine blades are often made of this type. These are martensitic stainless steels (one of the three possible crystal structures).

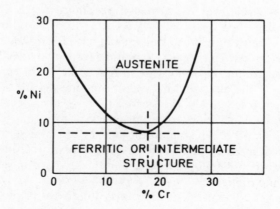

(1) Graph showing the various combinations of chromium and nickel that create austenitic stainless steel.

Another group of stainless steels are of the 17% chromium (no nickel) ferritic type, used for car trim because it has good resistance to atmospheric corrosion. Then there are the 17% chromium, 2% nickel martensitic types which have high strength and are used for aircraft fasteners.

Unlike the brasses and bronzes which are labelled with names ('aluminium brass', 'silicon bronze' etc) giving sufficient accuracy of definition for many purposes, stainless steels are unfortunately only known by numbers.

The American Iron and Steel Institute (AISI) and the British Standards (BS) numbers are nowadays most commonly referred to:

AISI numbers	% Chromium	% Nickel	
500 series	4–6		
400 series	11–27	0–2.5	Ferritic or Martensitic
200 series	16–19	3–8	Austenitic due to manganese
300 series	16–26	6–22	Austenitic nickel stabilized

A 'true' (i.e. non-rusting) stainless steel contains more than 12% chromium.

A 'seagoing marine' stainless steel is austenitic.

Austenitic Stainless Steels: The Marine Grades

Turning now to the austenitic alloys, which are the ones of prime interest to us, of course there are many grades. The 'lowest' grade is 18/8 of which commercial varieties include Staybrite and Anka. This basic alloy although 'rust-free' has two problems: it is subject to 'weld decay'; it is very liable to pitting corrosion. Both these faults need some explanation.

'Weld decay' is the common term (carbide precipitation is the more scientific term) for the lowering of corrosion resistance of a narrow band adjacent to a weld. When, say, two plates are welded together, the adjacent metal is heated by the process and then slowly cooled. About 1–3 mm ($\frac{1}{16}$–$\frac{1}{8}$ in.) away from the weld the

17

temperature goes through a critical range (850°–550°C) and this produces chromium carbide at the grain boundaries. In the process carbon atoms diffuse rapidly from the grains to the grain boundaries but the chromium atoms are drawn slowly from the narrow bands adjacent to the weld. What this metallurgical language means is that the strips of metal close to the weld are impoverished of chromium and so the corrosion resistance there is very low (2). And also these strips are galvanically less noble than the parent stainless steel. On both counts the effect is disastrous when the welded fitting is put into service, perhaps helping to hold up a mast. Subjected to a salty environment and stressed, intercrystalline cracks can form causing the component to break. In bad cases the metal actually crumbles to powder.

The problem is that weld decay is not readily apparent. When new there is nothing to be seen by the naked eye and even a strength test will not necessarily reveal a weakness. It is only in a corrosive environment and after some time that the trouble shows itself – too late of course.

This is a problem that metallurgists have now overcome, and it is only necessary to specify the right kind of stainless in order to avoid the trouble. But before talking about these grades let us consider the other major defect of stainless steel: pitting corrosion.

The tough oxide film created by the chromium content is maintained by oxygen. The oxygen comes from the air, or if the steel is immersed it comes from the water. Generally there is enough oxygen in water to keep fish alive and to maintain that oxide film on the exposed surface of stainless steel. Problems arise if the

CARBIDE PRECIPITATION

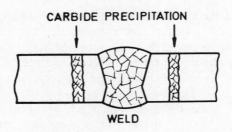

WELD

(2) Weld decay in stainless steel. This causes sudden failure later under stress and corrosion. The correct grade of stainless should be chosen when welding is performed.

oxygen level, local to the surface of the metal, drops. This can happen under barnacles or dirt or weed, or in crevices perhaps created by a bolted fitting, or by a poor surface finish. These small areas lose their oxide film and the underlying metal is exposed. Unfortunately this matters a great deal because the exposed metal is less noble than the surrounding large noble area, which as explained in Chapter 7 on Galvanic Corrosion, is death. The result is that the small area corrodes very rapidly and a pit develops (3). Depending on the type of stainless steel, the pitting can perforate thin plate in a matter of months in seawater.

Preventing Weld Decay

There are three ways of doing this: (a) solution annealing; (b) restricting the carbon content; (c) adding stabilizing elements. Solution annealing means that the welded item is heated to 1050°C, where the carbides are in solution, and then quenched in water. The object is to cool the metal so quickly that the chromium and carbon atoms do not have time to combine and form an area prone to weld decay. Contrary to its effect on most other materials, this treatment softens stainless steel. It is limited to fabricated items that have only thin parts; thicker metal will cool too slowly, even in water.

Restricting the carbon content is obviously one way to avoid weld decay. Whereas most of the austenitic stainless steels have

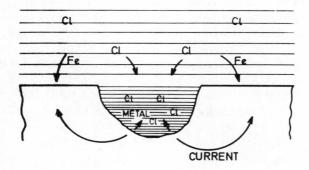

(3) The corrosion mechanism inside a pit in stainless steel.

0.06–0.12% carbon (C), if this is reduced to 0.03%C weld decay does not happen. However, when welding is being carried out carbon must not be allowed to be picked up from the process by the metal. In other words gas welding is not advised: use electric welding with a covered electrode, a submerged arc, or inert gas. The AISI type stainless steels which have the suffix 'L' are those with a low carbon content.

The last method of preventing weld decay is to add very small quantities of elements which have a greater affinity for carbon than chromium. Thus the carbon is 'stabilized' by these elements and prevented from combining with the chromium. Titanium (Ti) and niobium (Cb) are two such elements. (Niobium is sometimes called columbium.) To do its job the amount of titanium needs to be five times the carbon content, and ten times in the case of niobium. AISI Types 321 and 347 are examples.

To sum up, weld decay ought not to be a problem today with marine stainless steel fittings because the problem is well known, and the manufacturers of the fitting ought to be using stabilized stainless steel or a low-carbon stainless steel, or quenching, if there is any welding performed on the item during production.

Pitting Corrosion

On the other hand, pitting corrosion in seawater is a problem that has not been solved. Some stainless steels are more resistant than others; some scientists claim to have found the answer with newly-developed stainless steels, but these are not yet readily available.

Much research has gone on for many years on the subject of pitting corrosion. Stainless steel is very popular for the construction of heat exchangers, tanks and condensers for power stations and desalination plants using salt and fresh water. Much of this is in the form of thin-walled tubing through which hot seawater flows. Pitting of the walls can soon cause a leak and perhaps the shutdown of the entire plant. The literature on this subject is vast; however, the research and conclusions are also valid for stainless steel parts fastened underwater on a boat.

To dwell for a moment on the mechanism of pitting corrosion in close-up – under a magnifying glass as it were – an electric cell is set up as soon as a break occurs in the hard oxide film (3). The cell is driven by the oxygen creating a concentration of chloride ions. The higher the chloride content of the water the greater the activity of the cell. Within the pit the chloride ions concentrate and the attack on the metal inside the crater increases. Once started, the situation gets steadily worse. The voltage of this electric cell varies up to 0.5 volts, which in galvanic terms is a large voltage for an anode and cathode in such close proximity.

Sometimes one sees stainless steels labelled 'active' or 'passive' and these terms refer to whether the metal is exposed at the surface (active) or covered with the tough oxide film (passive). Active stainless steel appears lower down (less noble) in the galvanic series, but this is not the basic place for stainless steel in the series when comparing metal with metal for galvanic compatability. Because the chromium combines so rapidly with oxygen the oxide film is normally there – unless lack of oxygen causes a breach and pits develop.

Scientists now make the distinction between 'crevice corrosion' and 'pitting'. Crevice corrosion takes place when a definite shielding of the oxide film occurs, thus starving the metal of oxygen. This can happen under a bolt head or washer, around the shank of a wood screw or under a barnacle. Pitting, on the other hand, can take place on the exposed clear surface. But it takes a more corrosive environment, like a higher salt (chloride) content, to cause pitting rather than crevice corrosion. Put a piece of stainless steel in seawater and pits first start under or in crevices; later on, or if the corrosive environment gets worse, pits may develop on the clean surface of the metal.

The standard laboratory test for 'pitting resistance' is to put a rubber band around the stainless specimen and immerse it in ferric chloride solution. Low-grade stainless steels succumb within hours. It is reckoned that any steel that can withstand the test without pitting is good enough for underwater marine use anywhere in the world.

Many long-term seawater tests have been carried out; samples have been placed in seawater in various parts of the world and left there for years. The results are quite illuminating and are shown in Table 1. In these cases the specimens were immersed in *quiet* water rather than a steady flow (which is an important factor as I will describe in a moment), and they were allowed to grow foul with barnacles and weed.

Several conclusions can be drawn from tests like these. Pitting occurs in crevices on most specimens. The number of pits and the intensity of the attack is largely determined by the extent of fouling. The one element in the composition of the stainless steels that has a large effect is molybdenum (Mo). It reduces the probability of attack, but once a pit has developed it apparently has little effect in stopping the corrosion. Over the years, service experience in power stations, etc has confirmed that stainless steel containing molybdenum is less susceptible to crevice corrosion.

Type 304 stainless steel is typical of the 18/8 alloys; Type 316 contains molybdenum. These are the two most common 'marine grade' stainless steels, 316 being better than 304.

Being developed (or at least being tested in service) are better types containing more molybdenum or more chromium or more nickel, or a combination of all three. They are not commonly available at the moment, but just to complete the picture it is worth mentioning some of them, and comparing their composition percentages with Type 316:

	Cr	Ni	Mo	Mn	C
Type 316	17	12	2.5	2	.08
Ferralium 225	25	5.5	3	2	.08
AL 6X	20	24	6.5	1.5	.03
26–1s	26	–	1	–	.06 + Ti
Du Pont 29–4	29	–	4	–	.01
Alloy 20	20	29	2	–	– + Nb

Most of these are proprietory alloys that are not yet standardized; Alloy 20 is commercially available and has the best resistance to crevice corrosion of the commonly used stainless steels. 26–1s and 29–4 have no nickel content and are actually ferritic grades. Both AL-6X and 29–4 have been proved in service and should make their mark in the commercial world in years to come. High-alloy grades will obviously cost more; half the composition of Alloy 20 is of expensive chromium and nickel.

Ferralium is commercially available. It is very resistant to crevice corrosion, and has a very high corrosion fatigue strength of 20 tons per square inch.

Velocity Effects

The tests mentioned in Table 1 involved still or 'quiet' water. If the water or the stainless item is continuously moving the chance of barnacles or silt becoming attached is lessened. Also the water is more likely to be aerated and contain more oxygen. Stagnant water may have only a tenth of the oxygen content of flowing water (hence the need for fish-tank aerators). So on both counts stainless steel is much less likely to pit in flowing water. In one particular test Type 316 plate was immersed in seawater flowing at $2\frac{1}{2}$ knots for $3\frac{1}{2}$ years without any sign of pitting. Similar pieces left in static seawater had many pits up to 3 mm ($\frac{1}{8}$ in.) deep. Unlike other metals which do not rely on an oxide film for protection, stainless steel revels in a flow of water. Whereas copper erodes away at speeds above about 3 knots, stainless steel has a remarkably low rate of overall corrosion up to 80 knots at least; little is known beyond. Hence it is used for propellers, pump parts and condenser tubing. Unfortunately for boat use, the fact that stainless steel is virtually corrosion-free in flowing water is of little consequence since for most of her life a pleasure boat is sitting idly at her moorings in quiet water.

Surface Finish

Although it is known that the oxide film is thickened and toughened by polishing to a mirror finish, according to some tests this has little effect on the probability of pitting. This only applies to the *surface finish* of a flat plate; clumsy weld beads and rough cut edges are invitations for crevice corrosion and need to be ground smooth and into a fair shape. Possibly the truth of the matter is that providing austenitic stainless steel is at least pickled to a bright finish its performance will not be improved by polishing. Polishing to a mirror finish is attractive but will not enhance resistance to pitting.

Electro-polishing is a process often used after a complex article is manufactured, in order to produce a polished surface, rather than buffing and hand polishing. For people who make up their own bits and pieces in stainless it is possible to electro-polish at home.

THE METALS THEMSELVES

Electro-polishing is the opposite to electro-plating; in other words metal is taken *off* the item rather than deposited *on* it. The roughness is preferentially eroded producing a smoother and smoother surface.

The item is immersed in an acid solution and connected to the positive terminal of a 12V car battery. The other terminal is connected to a sheet of lead surrounding the item (4).

The acid solution should be: 65% Technical Grade phosphoric acid, SG (specific gravity) 1.7; 20% sulphuric acid SG, 1.84; 15% water (percentages by volume). (The complete solution can be made up by a friendly chemist.) Avoid immersing any iron or steel in the solution (e.g. the clip onto the item from the battery lead). Ideally the current should be between 1 and 5 amps per square inch (0.15–0.8 amps per sq cm) of surface area, so an ammeter is needed in the circuit. However the current 'density' is not very critical. The current can be varied by varying the voltage tapped off the car battery: hence it is handy to use the type of battery where each cell's terminals are accessible. The solution should be hot, about 70°–90°C. Degrease the item in acetone and thereafter avoid touching it with fingers. The time taken will vary up to about an hour, depending on the current and temperature. To increase the

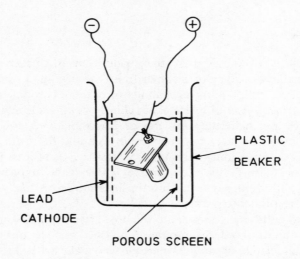

(4) Simple electropolishing.

rate of polishing in areas that are in 'shadow', a lead paddle can be made up wrapped in a porous cloth (to avoid accidentally touching the item and causing a short circuit). This is connected to the negative of the battery and then moved around close to the duller areas until they are bright.

As a matter of interest, coloured stainless steel is now commercially available. The colour is made by immersion in a special hot acid solution and black and various shiny hues can be produced. Developed for architectural purposes for internal and external decoration, it might one day spread into the yacht world as did coloured anodizing.

Temperature

So far I have not mentioned the effect of temperature. As the working temperature increases so too does the chance of pitting: hence to avoid pitting a superior steel must be used. A combination of static seawater and high temperature will cause just about any type of stainless steel to pit, but it is difficult to think of that situation occurring on a boat. An exhaust pipe of stainless steel will at least have *flowing* hot water and for not many hours at that compared to the cooling tubes of power stations running twenty-four hours a day. For instance a typical performance of Type 316 tubes in a power station would be numerous small pits at a density of up to eight per sq cm, but none more than 0.5 mm (0.02 in.) deep after eighteen months' continual use. It is when the boat's engine is stopped and a pool of seawater lies stagnant inside the exhaust pipe that conditions are ripe for bad pitting. Obviously the run of the pipe ought to be designed to avoid water traps.

Galvanic Behaviour

Passive stainless steel (with its oxide layer intact) is high up in the galvanic scale (for explanation of the galvanic scale refer to Chapter 7 on Galvanic Corrosion). On the other hand, because of its oxide skin it causes less galvanic corrosion when coupled to less noble metals in seawater than one would suppose. The following table based on test results illustrates this fact.

Metals in contact	Corrosion rate of steel: mm per year
Mild steel by itself	0.79 mm
Mild steel with Type 304	0.91 mm
Mild steel with titanium	1.07 mm
Mild steel with copper	2.54 mm

The seawater in this test was flowing at $4\frac{1}{2}$ knots. Also the surface areas of the opposing metals were the same, i.e. the area ratio was 1:1, the significance of which is explained in chapter 7.

Another aspect that has important consequences is that it has been shown that when stainless steel is in contact with a less noble metal the risk of pitting is much reduced. Deliberate galvanic or cathodic protection also does the trick. What this means in practice is that stainless steel can be used with more confidence underwater where it is surrounded by a large less noble area, for example a stainless steel rudder or propeller or propeller shaft on a steel or aluminium hull. The risk of pitting corrosion on the stainless item will be much less than for a similar fitting on a fibreglass hull.

One test which shows this point was as follows. Type 304 specimens were left in quiet seawater for 490 days with and without cathodic protection. The protection was afforded by iron and aluminium anodes. The area ratio was 1:9 (anode:cathode).

	Depth of attack (mils)	
	crevices	pits
No cathodic protection	62	4
Iron anode	1	3
Aluminium anode	1	1

This phenomenon is borne out in practice; and so, although it is basically unsound to use stainless underwater, incidental or deliberate galvanic protection considerably reduces the risk of pitting. The following combinations are therefore permissible:

Stainless propeller shafts and rudders and propellers on a steel or aluminium hull (and electrically coupled).

The same items on a fibreglass hull with zinc or aluminium sacrificial anodes wired up.

Stainless bolts in an aluminium outdrive.

Corrosion being as capricious as it is, hard and fast rules always have exceptions. There is no guarantee that galvanic protection will be the full answer to a particular problem. I can recall at least one failure of a Type 316 stainless propeller shaft that *did* have zinc collars attached.

Stress Corrosion

The combination of a corrosive environment and continual high stress leads to cracking and complete failure of many metals. Stainless steel Types 304 and 316 in seawater are only prone to stress corrosion at higher temperatures: the limit is often quoted as 66°C (150°F). Generally at normal temperatures austenitic stainless steel on boats is free from this particular bugbear. However, the possibility of stress corrosion cracking, particularly of items of stainless steel rigging, should not be dismissed lightly. Failure is sudden and can be disastrous. The factors that can promote cracking are (a) concentrated chlorides – in other words damp salt; (b) a weld, causing locked-in stress or roughness to promote pitting from which cracks can start (weld decay is also a possibility); (c) a stress concentration caused by poor design – e.g. a notch or sharp corner, or even a thread; (d) machining grades of stainless; (e) a hot climate. The most important of these causes are improper design and manufacture.

Corrosion Fatigue

This is the combination of corrosion and stress cycling; in other words the load in the metal is constantly changing (as when you break a paperclip by bending it back and forth). The fatigue stress that stainless steel can endure without cracking in air is much reduced when it is placed in seawater, or for that matter covered in moist sea salt. But it is really no worse than other metals; in fact it is a lot better than manganese bronze and unprotected mild steel.

The list of trouble makers mentioned under 'stress corrosion' applies equally to corrosion fatigue; to them should be added stress cycling, the continual slight bending back and forth. This sort of loading often occurs through vibration caused by the engine or by wind. Chainplates and mast tangs made of strip metal are classic examples of components subject to corrosion fatigue.

Stainless wire rope used underwater in seawater has been found to fail in a very short time, especially if it is a working rope and continually flexed. The combination of thin individual wires packed together causing crevices with flexing and salt water proves too much. Above water it is universally used and long-lasting. Terminals, however, need to be packed and sealed to prevent crevices. Stress corrosion and corrosion fatigue are also discussed in Chapter 6 on Types of Corrosion.

Cavitation

Stainless steel has been found to be one of the best materials to resist cavitation erosion. Together with its high strength and corrosion resistance and its ease of repair, Type 304 is popular for propellers. It has also been used for cladding areas on mild steel plate that have been eroded by cavitation, such as mild steel rudders eroded by the propeller slipstream. The cladding is often deposited by weld metal, in the form of runs of weld alongside each other and ground off flush afterwards.

Fresh Waters

In all the foregoing I have been talking about stainless steel in relation to seawater. The situation in fresh water is markedly happier. Earlier in this chapter I mentioned that the chloride level in the water is an important factor in the mechanism of pitting corrosion. Seawater has around 19,000 parts per million (ppm) of chloride, though this varies around the world and especially in river estuaries and harbours where mixing with fresh water takes place. Authorities quote 1,000 ppm as the level below which Type 304 (18/8) can be used without risk of pitting. Non-tidal rivers, canals and lakes ought to be below this level. Thus the general conclusion is that 304 and 316 stainless steels can be used for underwater fittings in fresh waters.

In fact, above water poorer grades can be used successfully. After all, the corrosion environment is free of salt and unless the boat lives in an industrial area the atmosphere will be clean and not very corrosive. So the stainless steels with less chromium and nickel content, i.e. the non-austenitic types, are suitable for deck fittings. Type 430 represents the rock bottom; better are types 201 and 202; then 301 and 302; and finally the best, 304 and 316.

Magnetic Properties

Austenitic stainless steels are basically non-magnetic. This is a useful property to remember because with a magnet one can test whether an item is actually made of austenitic rather than ferritic and martensitic stainless (both magnetic). Cast austenitic stainless steel may contain some ferritic and may therefore be slightly attracted to a magnet. In sheet or tube form ('wrought') and annealed, stainless is virtually non-magnetic although some types like 304 become slightly magnetic when cold-worked. Type 316, however, does not exhibit this tendency.

Standards

The number of different types of stainless steel available around the world is bewildering. Many have been formally standardized by the various standards institutes in individual countries and Tables 2 and 3 are a guide here. However the two that are most appropriate and commonly available for marine use are Type 304 and 316. These are the AISI (American Iron and Steel Institute) standards and are equivalent to British Standards EN58E and EN58J respectively, although these notations have been superceded in British Standards by 304S15 and 316S16 respectively. These two type numbers are often quoted when tubing or deck fittings, etc are advertised.

Sometimes Type 304 is referred to simply as 18/8. Similarly, Type 316 is sometimes referred to as 18/10/3 or 'molybdenum stabilized' stainless steel.

Care of Stainless

Even if the item is above water it is good practice to clean and smooth welds and any rough edges. Rust stains sometimes appear on new items and may be due to particles of iron or steel embedded in the surface during the manufacturing process. Wire-brushing with dilute nitric acid should remove the stains (beware acid getting in eyes or on clothes). To retain a good appearance one can rub down stainless steel with dilute nitric acid every few months, but naturally one has to be careful not to allow the acid to get anywhere else on the boat, so wet the surroundings first and then wash off afterwards with copious amounts of water. Staining usually stops after a few months, and it has been found that Type 316 is less liable to stain than 304.

Proprietory cleaners are usually quite good at removing rust stains, however. They usually originate in crevices rather than on a smooth surface. Where a stainless item has not been bedded down and water can penetrate, rust 'bleeds' can appear. The only answer is to take off the fitting, paint the underside with zinc chromate and refit it with a flexible bedding compound.

Similarly it is wise to grease threads with a zinc chromate grease, partly to fill the crevices and partly to reduce the chance of seizure.

To Draw Some Conclusions

Stainless steel is fine for deck fittings: virtually corrosion-free and yet strong. The two common 'marine' grades are Type 304 and 316, the latter being the best. Both types suffer from pitting corrosion when immersed in seawater and are therefore basically unsuited for any underwater part of a boat. This applies especially to fastenings in wet wood or in fibreglass. The situation is not nearly so bad if the fastening is used in steel or aluminium or any metal less noble than stainless; stainless bolts in an aluminium outdrive are an example. Again, if the surface of the stainless steel is exposed to a flow of water, as on a rudder blade for example, pitting may not cause trouble. 'Free machining' grades (e.g. Type 303) can be less corrosion resistant; this applies for example to bolts machined from bar. On deck or below water always use a flexible sealant under mounting pads, etc.

If an item is to be welded it must be made of Type 304L or 316L (low-carbon), or stabilized (Type 321 or Type 347), or heat-treated afterwards, otherwise weld decay is likely to cause the fitting to break suddenly one day when under load.

Similarly, stress corrosion and corrosion fatigue can cause sudden breakage, and it has been said that some round-the-world yachtsmen prefer not to have highly stressed stainless steel fittings like toggles and rigging screws in their standing rigging. However, the evidence such as it is suggests that properly designed and made stainless items of Type 316 are no more likely to fail than ones made from galvanized steel or manganese bronze.

It is vital to be sure of the grade of stainless steel because there are so many alloys, and yet so few suitable for exterior use on yachts moored in salt water. Type 316 is currently the best commonly available. Better types will probably follow in the future.

Table 1
Pitting of Stainless Steel Plates Left Immersed in Quiet Seawater

| | | Depth of pitting (mm) | | | | |
| | | Under fouling | | In crevices | | |
AISI Type	Duration of tests (days)	max.	average	max.	average	Remarks
302	643	P*	0.79	—	—	plain 18/8 1.3 mm thick
304	320	0.99	0.56	0.91	0.6	18/8
304	365	P	P	—	—	18/8 1.6 mm thick
347	755	2.0	1.4	1.2	0.9	weld stabilized 18/10
321	944	1.4	0.4	1.4	0.6	weld stabilized 18/10
316	365	1.4	0.3	1.4	1.4	2–3% molybdenum
316	730	0.7	0.3	1.4	1.4	,, ,,
316	1255	1.3	0.6	4.3	1.2	,, ,,
316	2773	0.8	0.4	—	—	,, ,,
316	3164	0.6	0.3	—	—	3.18% Mo
317	1075	0.6	0.3	1.1	0.7	11–15% Ni, 3–4% Mo
305	198	0.1	0.05	—	—	10–13% Ni
308	755	5.2	2.1	3.6	1.7	19/10 Cr/Ni
309	320	0.7	0.3	P	P	22/12 Cr/Ni 1.4 mm thick
310	320	0.2	0.07	P	P	24/19 Cr/Ni 0.6 mm thick
329	106	0	0	0.9	0.9	23/2.5 Cr/Ni

*P = perforated

Table 2
Nearest Foreign Equivalents of AISI Austenitic Stainless Steels

USA	UK (old)	UK (new)	France	Germany	Italy	Sweden	Japan
AISI	En		AFNOR	VD Eh	UNI	SIS	JIS
301			Z 12 CN 18–8	X 12 Cr Ni 17–7	X 15 CN 1707	2330 2331	SUS 39
302	58A	302S25	Z 12 CN 18–10	X 12 Cr Ni 18–8	X 15 CN 1808	2330 2331	SUS 40
303	58M	303S21 303S41 325S21		X 12 Cr Ni 18–8			
304	58E	304S15	Z 6 CN 18–10	X 5 Cr Ni 18–9	X 8 CN 1910	2332	SUS 27
304L		304S12	Z 3 CN 18–10		X 3 CN 1911		SUS 28
309	55		Z 15 CNS 25–13	X 15 Cr Ni Si 20–12	X 20 CN 2412		
309S							SUS 41
310			Z 15 CNS 25–20	X 15 Cr Ni Si 25–20	X 25 CN 2520	2361	
310S							SUS 42
314				X 15 Cr Ni Si 25–20		2361	
316	58H 58J	315S16 316S16 320S17	Z 6 CND 18–12	X 5 Cr Ni Mo 18–12	X 8 CND 1712	2342	SUS 32
316L		316S12	Z 3 CND 18–12	X 3 Cr Ni Mo 18–13			SUS 33
317	58J	316S16 320S17		X 5 Cr Ni Mo 17–13			
318			Z 8 CNDNb 18–12	X 10 Cr Ni Mo Nb 18–12		2343	
321	58B 58C	321S12 321S20	Z 10 CNT 18–10	X 10 Cr Ni Ti 18–9	X 8 CNT 1810	2333 2334	SUS 29
330			Z 20 NCS 36–18				
347	58F 58G	347S17	Z 10 CNNb 18–10	X 10 Cr Ni Nb 18–9	X 8 CNNb 1811	2333 2334	SUS 43

32

Table 3

AISI Standard Composition for Wrought Austenitic Stainless Steels

% composition (Fe remainder with maxima for impurities)

Casting alloy equivalent	AISI Type	Cr	Ni	Mo	Other	Remarks
	201	16.00–18.00	3.50– 5.50	—	N 0.25 max	+ high
	202	17.00–19.00	4.00– 6.00	—	N 0.25 max	manganese
	301	16.00–18.00	6.00– 8.00	—	—	
CF20	302	17.00–19.00	8.00–10.00	—	—	general purpose 18/8
	302B	17.00–19.00	8.00–10.00	—	—	
CF16F	303	17.00–19.00	8.00–10.00	0.60 max	S 0.15 min	free machin-
	303Se	17.00–19.00	8.00–10.00	—	Se 0.15 min	ing grades
CF 8	304	18.00–20.00	8.00–12.00	—	—	'marine' 18/8
CF3	304L	18.00–20.00	8.00–12.00			low carbon for welding
	305	17.00–19.00	10.00–13.00	—	—	
	308	19.00–21.00	10.00–12.00	—	—	
CH 20	309	22.00–24.00	12.00–15.00	—	—	
	309S	22.00–24.00	12.00–15.00	—	—	for high temperatures
CK20	310	24.00–26.00	19.00–22.00	—	—	
	310S	24.00–26.00	19.00–22.00	—	—	
	314	23.00–26.00	19.00–22.00	—	—	
CF8M/ 12M	316	16.00–18.00	10.00–14.00	2.00–3.0	—	'marine'* 18/10/3
CF3M	316L	16.00–18.00	10.00–14.00	2.00–3.00	—	low carbon for welding
CG8M	317	18.00–20.00	11.00–15.00	3.00–4.00	—	high molybdenum
	D319	17.40–19.50	11.00–15.00	2.25–3.00	—	
	321	17.00–19.00	9.00–12.00	—	Ti	
CF8C	347	17.00–19.00	9.00–13.00	—	Cb-Ta	stabilized for welding
	348	17.00–19.00	9.00–13.00	—	Cb-Ta/Co	

Note: * The 'marine' molybdenum-bearing stainless steels can be identified by smearing on a proprietory compound (e.g. DL 12) which is turned brown by the presence of molybdenum. Comparing the brown colour with the colour given by a piece of known Type 316 gives a rough guide as to the molybdenum content.

THE METALS THEMSELVES

For comparison with the 'marine' austenitic grades here are some non-austenitic grades:

AISI Type	Cr	Ni	Remarks
405	11.5–14.5	—	} Ferritic
430	14–18	—	
442	18–23	—	
403	11.5–13	—	} Martensitic
410	11.5–14.5	—	
416	12–14		
431	15–17	1.25–2.5	

Some of these, e.g. 430, are suitable for use on deck on fresh water craft.

Chapter 2
Copper and Nickel Based Alloys (Brasses and Bronzes)

Together with steels and aluminium alloys, the alloys based on copper and nickel are most often used in boats. Unlike the first two groups of metals the copper alloys have been used in boatbuilding for centuries, and with the exception of brass are still the best for any underwater metal part.

The range of different copper and nickel alloys that are available makes confusing reading and this introduction to them attempts to sort them into groups and then tackle each group in turn.

First there is copper itself, then the alloy of copper and zinc called brass, then the copper-based alloys that do *not* use zinc (e.g. the bronzes), and finally the nickel-based alloys (e.g. Monel). All four groups of alloys are often loosely referred to as 'non-ferrous', and the brasses are often referred to as 'yellow metal' because of their yellowy colour. ('Non-ferrous' means that this alloy does not contain iron, and is also applicable to other metals such as aluminium or magnesium.)

Categories of copper and nickel based alloys
Copper

Brasses	Copper-zinc alloys including naval brass and manganese 'bronze'.
Zinc-free copper alloys	Bronze, gunmetal and copper-nickel.
Nickel-based alloys	Monel, et al.

THE METALS THEMSELVES

Copper

A familiar material, soft, easily bent and not very strong. Exposed to the weather, the surface soon becomes green with a not unattractive patina. It has held together countless boats over the centuries, both clinker and carvel, by being used in nails and clenches. Such fasteners will often last as long as the boat, which is the best testimonial one could wish for!

Copper was also used extensively for sheathing the bottoms of wooden sailing ships and boats, partly to prevent worms from reaching the timber, especially in tropical waters; and partly to inhibit marine growth, because copper has a strong antifouling effect, equivalent to or better than modern antifouling paints. Copper sheathing has gone out of fashion nowadays although there are many copper-sheathed wooden craft still afloat that were built before fibreglass came on the scene. This topic is discussed more fully in Chapter 12 on Metal Hulls.

Perhaps the most common use for copper in boats today is in engine water piping, where unfortuantely it is not quite so suitable because of its susceptibility to impingement attack. Fast-flowing turbulent water first erodes the protective oxide layer away and then the copper metal. For piping, the flow rate should not exceed about 3 ft/sec (1 m/sec), the limit for average flow down a straight pipe. At bends or restrictions local water speeds will be higher, so bends should be gentle and restrictions avoided. Engine cooling pipes should be sized and laid out with this speed limit in mind. The formula, gallons per minute = 2.04 x D^2 x V gives the relationship between flow speed and size of pipe. D is the internal bore in inches, V is speed in feet per second. (Or, litres per minute = 0.047 x D^2 x V where D is in millimetres and V is metres per second.)

As in domestic water systems, copper piping is useful for the fresh water supply on a boat. It is 'light-tight' (unlike clear plastic piping) which discourages the breeding of unwanted organisms. The copper itself is also beneficial in this respect.

The term 'copper' embraces three commercial varieties. The most common is 'de-ozidized non-arsenical' which is 99.9% copper and is used for general plumbing, and is good for welding. 'De-ozidized arsenical copper' is used where strength at high temperatures is important, e.g. in boilers. 'High conductivity copper' is used for

36

electrical purposes. As far as we are concerned the first variety is what we commonly term 'copper'.

Copper corrodes evenly in quiet seawater; pitting and crevice corrosion are no problem. On the other hand it is quite sensitive to hydrogen sulphide and ammonia, found in polluted water; the rate of corrosion increases dramatically as does the corrosion rate of most copper-based alloys. For instance, polluted seawater lying in engine cooling pipes can cause severe corrosion.

Brasses

Brass is a mixture or alloy of copper and zinc. Not only does the zinc add strength to copper but it also makes the product cheaper. The general resistance to atmospheric corrosion is maintained and so is the ease of working. The zinc content changes the rich red colour of copper to a yellower shade.

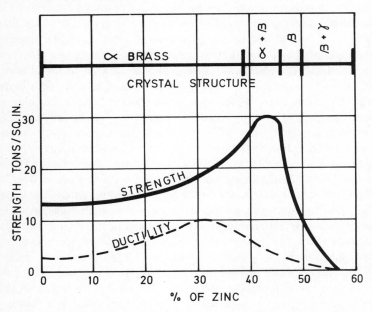

(5) Copper-zinc alloy diagram showing that 70/30 brass is most ductile and 60/40 is strongest.

The actual zinc content may be anything up to about 50%. Depending on the amount of zinc different crystal structures are formed, giving markedly different properties. Two distinct types are commonly used, namely the 70/30 and 60/40 types, sometimes called Alpha and Alpha-Beta brasses respectively. The 70/30 Alpha brasses (containing 30% zinc) are most ductile (they stretch easily) while the 60/40 are strongest (5). Other names for these two basic types of brass are Cartridge brass for the 70/30 (because gun cartridges must be very ductile when the gun fires) and Muntz metal for the 60/40. Both types are used in boat equipment.

Before starting a saga through the various brasses within these two broad groups, the most important disadvantage of brasses should be stated clearly. Brass should not be used underwater because it 'dezincifies'. Dezincification is the gradual dissolving of the zinc content of brass leaving a spongy mass of copper: although the shape of the article is retained its strength is virtually nil. The greater the zinc content of the brass the greater the chance of this happening. Such superior-sounding brasses as Admiralty or naval brass or manganese 'bronze' are not immune and, like stainless steel, should not be used underwater. But, also like stainless steel, there is evidence that when galvanically protected brass will not dezincify. If electrically linked to a large area of metal about 0.2 volts lower down the galvanic scale, the zinc will not dissolve out. In practice this means that a manganese bronze propeller or naval brass keel rubbing band on a *steel* boat will be all right. But on wood or fibreglass boats never use brass underwater, unless sacrificial anodes are fitted and wired up to the brass items.

In practical terms a manganese bronze propeller shaft or propeller can be used on a steel boat, or on a fibreglass or wooden boat providing a sacrificial anode is fitted and wired up. But never use brass screws or bolts underwater on wood or fibreglass hulls, or any brass item underwater unless it is galvanically protected. Even then there is no guarantee that dezincification will not occur; it is far better in the long run to avoid brass (and stainless steel) for underwater uses, or any location which is constantly wet.

Having got that message home, another vital point to note is that manganese bronze is *not* a bronze; it is a brass. The term 'bronze' has always indicated a superior metal and no doubt some unscrupulous character in the dim past thought he would call his product 'manganese bronze' in the hope of deceiving people. Manganese bronze is a 60/40 brass and dezincifies readily.

✳ De-zincification is a long-standing problem of brasses and many attempts have been made to reduce the tendency by adding small amounts of other elements, because otherwise brasses are excellent materials. The better ones are as strong as mild steel, *generally* corrosion resistant and yet not too expensive.

The greater the amount of zinc the greater the chance of de-zincification occurring. A brass with less than 15% is usually immune. The 70/30 types are inherently better than the 60/40 types, and can in fact be successfully used underwater if inhibited with a trace of arsenic (0.02–0.06%). The problem, however, is how does one know whether that trace is there when buying some item at the chandler's counter?

The 60/40 brasses cannot be inhibited entirely, although the addition of 1% tin does help a little. However, its effect is not enough. Naval brass is an example of this.

Brasses are fairly susceptible to stress corrosion, the combined effect of stress and a corrosive agent. With brass this is often called 'season cracking' and occurs especially in brass that has been cold-worked and consequently has 'locked-up' internal stresses. Season cracking of brass rifle cartridges was a great problem during the First World War; the brass cases would crack even before they got to the front. Prompt annealing at 200°–300°C after manufacture is one answer to the problem, but even nowadays brass can fail. One sometimes hears comments such as 'It suddenly turned brittle and fell apart in my hand' or 'It went crystaline'. This is season cracking. The particular agents that cause trouble are ammonia, mercury and seawater and polluted waste. A tightened-up bolt when attacked by such agents can have its head fall off. Again, this is another reason for not using brass underwater. Season cracking is more likely with the cheaper high-zinc brasses.

The most common brasses are:

	Cu/Zn %
Cartridge brass	70/30
Muntz metal	60/40
Admiralty brass	70/30
Naval brass (or Tobin bronze)	60/40

Aluminium brass	76/22
Manganese bronze (or High-tensile brass)	60/40

Cartridge brass has already been mentioned. Together with the other Alpha brasses – Admiralty and aluminium brass – they are reasonably resistant to dezincification if inhibited with arsenic. *Inhibited Admiralty brass* was so-called because it was developed for the British Navy about sixty years ago for steam turbine condensers to avoid dezincification. *Aluminium brass* is perhaps the best brass of all; the aluminium content gives extra strength, the low zinc content a lower risk of dezincification. But arsenic should ideally be present. The presence of aluminium makes it difficult to solder. It is used in ships for pipework and condensers as it has a high resistance to impingement attack (up to 10 ft/sec or 3m/sec) and a low risk of dezincification, but it is still not as good as the copper-nickels. It offers a halfway house in terms of cost and performance between Admiralty brass and copper-nickels.

A proprietary brass that is often come across is Tungum (a trade name of Tungum Hydraulics Ltd). This is a low-zinc brass with a maximum of 16.7% zinc. It also has a small percentage of aluminium, nickel and silicon. It is as strong as mild steel, very ductile and resistant to fatigue. It performs well in seawater, dezincification not being a problem. Tungum used to be used rather than copper for sheathing fast wooden boats, because of its better resistance to a fast flow of water. Sheet is mechanically stronger than copper and the metal is more resistant to erosion. Nowadays Tungum is often used for salt water piping, and high pressure piping.

The three 60/40 brasses in the list are poorer metals; *naval brass* should have tin to reduce the great susceptibility of this Muntz-type metal to dezincification. *Manganese bronze* is the black sheep of the family and is actually a high-zinc brass with the addition of manganese to increase its strength up to that of mild steel. For deck fittings, rigging screws, etc it is a good material, stronger than gunmetal and relatively inexpensive. It is also commonly used for propeller shafts and propellers, and although this is basically a mistake cathodic protection can give a reasonable life in seawater. *Nickel-manganese bronze* is a higher strength version of manganese bronze sometimes used for propellers.

Finally one copper-base alloy that ought to be mentioned for completeness is *nickel silver* or *'German silver'*. It is a low-zinc brass with 10–30% of nickel; it has a pleasant silvery-white appearance conferred by the nickel and is used for decorative and corrosion resistant items like nameplates on large motor yachts. There is no silver in the mix.

Zinc-Free Copper Alloys

In this category come the *bronzes*. To most people the term 'bronze' immediately conjures up a superior metal to a 'brass', and indeed the bronzes are superior in terms of corrosion resistance, although not always in terms of strength. The essential point is that they do not contain a significant amount of zinc so dezincification is not a problem.

Bronze Age bronze was an alloy of copper and tin but is not much used now because the addition of small quantities of other elements increases the strength without detriment in other respects, resulting in the 'gunmetals'.

The search for higher strength alloys that retained the corrosion resistance of ordinary bronze has led to the development of copper alloys that do not actually contain tin, so they cannot really be called bronzes. Silicon bronze is an example (96% Cu, 3% Si) and so too is aluminium bronze (90% Cu, 10% Al). Other copper alloys in the same class are correctly not called bronzes – the copper-nickels for example. The commonly used copper alloys are:

Gunmetal	88% Cu + Tin
Aluminium bronze	90% Cu + Aluminium
Nickel-aluminium bronze	85% Cu + Aluminium + Nickel
Silicon bronze	96% Cu + Silicon
Phosphor bronze	90% Cu + Tin + Phosphorus
90/10 Copper-nickel	90% Cu + Nickel
70/30 Copper-nickel	70% Cu + Nickel

Note the high percentage of copper in all of them. Unlike brass, the bronzes are not diluted with large amounts of cheap metal (zinc).

Consequently they are more expensive, but give better corrosion resistance.

Gunmetal was used, as its name suggests, for making guns in centuries gone by. It is a good casting metal, it has a lovely sheen (which tarnishes in sea air), and it is not prone to dezincification, stress corrosion, crevice corrosion or pitting. Because of its relatively low strength it is not good as a fastener material. Nowadays silicon bronze has superseded gunmetal as an all-round corrosion resistant fastener material; but for castings for such items as bollards, fairleads, seacocks, stern tubes, rudder tubes, etc gunmetal has great merit. It is a material that can confidently be used underwater.

There are several types of gunmetal but the common ones contain either 6% or 10% tin, in America commonly known as M bronze and G bronze respectively, but both have similar properties. Sometimes these are referred to as 'tin bronzes'.

Aluminium bronze (not to be confused with aluminium *brass*) is also a fine material with good resistance to pitting, fatigue and wear, and it has a lovely golden colour. It casts easily and is a little stronger than manganese bronze, and of course is not prone to dezincification. It is another material that can be used underwater although it has been known to be subject to 'de-aluminification', a ghastly word for a type of corrosion similar to dezincification. This, however, is avoided if 4% nickel is included in the mix. Added nickel also makes a stronger material, hence *Nickel-aluminium-bronze* (NAB for short). Similarly manganese will add strength, hence *nickel-aluminium-manganese bronze*. Propellers and propeller shafts and bolts can be bought in these materials and a very trouble-free life can be expected, but that old enemy manganese bronze is very much more commonly available – more's the pity. The aluminium bronzes are very resistant to pitting corrosion, crevice corrosion and water velocity effects and also stress corrosion.

Another good all-rounder is *silicon bronze*. Screws and barb-ring nails are readily available in this alloy; for example, Gripfast nails are made of a proprietory silicon bronze called Everdur. Silicon bronze can be used with confidence underwater.

Phosphor bronze castings are used for machined parts which need a bearing surface. Phosphor bronze makes a convenient corrosion resistant spring material and is found in such things as snap-shackles. It is a corrosion resistant as tin bronze since it has much the same basic composition.

The *copper-nickels* are a family with variations in the nickel content. They are basically very strong and entirely corrosion resistant, but of course are expensive and not normally used at the moment in the boating world. The main commerical use of this alloy is in tubing for carrying seawater in condensers of power stations and desalinators. Tubing is thus readily available commercially and so is plate, although they are not generally stocked by chandlers nor used by yacht equipment manufacturers.

The two varieties mostly produced are 70/30 and 90/10 (Cu/Ni). In general 70/30 is more corrosion resistant and stronger than 90/10 but more expensive. 90/10 is nevertheless as corrosion resistant as any boat owner could wish. A variety of even better copper-nickels are under development.

Nickel-Based Alloys

By itself nickel is a very corrosion resistant metal although it does suffer from pitting corrosion like stainless steel. When alloyed with copper a family of Ni/Cu metals are possible because unlike alloys of copper and zinc they are mutually soluble throughout their range and 'steps' are not present.

We have seen two commonly used alloys of copper and nickel with the 70/30 and 90/10 copper-nickels. These are at the 'coppery' end of the range. The nickel-based alloys are at the other end with 63-70% nickel, the remainder being copper (6).

The best known of the nickel-based alloys are the *Monel* series. The word Monel is a proprietary name. Seizing wire (by Ormiston), propeller shafts and hose clips and bolts of Monel are used on boats. It is a very strong and corrosion resistant material but of course expensive. It is very resistant to high water velocities and is therefore used for water pump parts.

There are two generally used Monels, Monel alloy 400, the 'ordinary' sort which is a basic 70/30 Ni/Cu alloy, and Monel alloy K500 or K Monel for short which is also a 70/30 but has 2-4% aluminium and is even stronger than Monel. There is also Monel

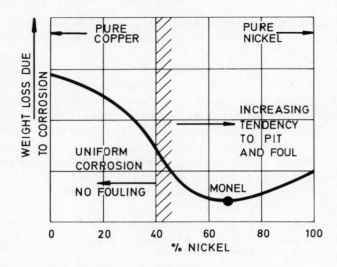

(6) Corrosion and the copper-nickel and nickel-copper alloys.

alloy 505 with silicon to make it even more resistant to erosion by water impingement. Various other nickel-based alloys are shown in Table 4. The ones with more than about 8% molybdenum are virtually inert in seawater, besides being of very high strength.

Although the Monels have a very low average corrosion rate, because of the high nickel content they do tend to pit in crevices. In one test a plate of Monel 400 was left immersed for a year after which time it had pitted slightly in many places, but the deepest pits were as much as 1.7 mm. While it is generally accepted that the Monels are excellent for propeller shafts, they are not perfect (as no metal is); but they are very strong, which is important for a propeller shaft on a fast boat. Pitting in Monel can be eliminated by deliberate galvanic protection sufficient to polarize it to 0.6–0.8 volts relative to a calomel reference electrode. A steeel hull, for instance, should prevent pitting of a Monel shaft.

It has been known for Monel propeller shafts to be badly pitted by polluted water containing hydrogen sulphide, but only in heavily polluted water very local to the boat and over a long period of time.

Apart from Monel, nickel-based alloys are infrequently used in boats because of their cost and availability, and perhaps because

they are too new to be established in the minds of the manufacturers of yacht equipment.

Chromium Plating

All of the copper alloys and Monel tarnish quickly in sea air and
eventually grow a verdigris of green salts. Frequent polishing is one
way to keep a bright appearance. Daily polishing of brasswork used
to be an endless chore for sailors in the Royal Navy: today effort
spent on this kind of exercise is diverted into more useful channels
and warships have very little brasswork. Few boat owners have the
urge to polish brasswork and hence the popularity, especially in the
1950s, of chromium plate. In its turn chromium plate is giving way
to stainless steel which is far more lasting in appearance.

There is more to chromium plating than meets the eye. The
chromium is best deposited on an intermediate metal, usually
nickel, because if the chromium layer is greater than about 0.00001
inches ($0.25\mu m$) thick, it tends to crack. The nickel layer is
therefore the main protection against corrosion of the basic metal,
and it is the thickness of this layer which is equally important. Any
surface damage is likely to affect both, however.

Modern techniques in chromium plating increase the corrosion
resistance of the nickel layer by depositing a double or triple layer
of nickel such that the upper layer corrodes preferentially.
Chromium layers can now be applied to a greater thickness without
cracking, or in another process deliberately cracked in a multitude
of tiny hairlines invisible to the naked eye to spread the corrosion
effect over a larger area.

ISO 1456–8 applies, and the relevant British Standard is BS 1224
and if an article is plated to this standard it ought to give good
service. But it is essential that the service grade number is stated
because there are four grades for varying conditions. Grade 1C is
the 'marine' grade; the other three (2C, 3C, 4C) are for prams and
office equipment! 'Plated to BS 1224 Grade 1C' is therefore a good
enough label for chromium plated items. The thickness of the
nickel layer and whether the chromium is 'micro-cracked' or
'double layer' are specified by a classification number for each
service grade, but it is the service grade that is most important.

45

THE METALS THEMSELVES

Nickel-chromium plating can be applied to other metals and the relevant marine service grade numbers are:

Steel	1S
Zinc	1Z
Copper alloys	1C
Aluminium	1A

Chromium plated items in the chandler's window or in his catalogue rarely say anything except 'chrome plated'. No mention of nickel nor a standard nor a service grade. One has to buy on trust, and all too often that trust is betrayed because after a season in a salty atmosphere the chromium becomes pitted and uncleanable. Or it may just peel off. Rubbing regularly with an oily rag or a wax polish will help to extend the life of the coating, but all too often this is impractical because of the shape of the item (a deck light protected by a wire grid, for example). Even in a protected place inside the wheelhouse or cabin, the type of chromium plate that is applied to yacht fittings fails after a few years. I think that unless one of the above standards is quoted, buying a chromium plated item is a waste of money, and a bare gunmetal or even brass fitting becomes less unsightly after a few years than poor quality chromium plate. Gunmetal actually produces little patina compared to brass and other copper alloys and dulls to a not unattractive finish.

In Fresh Water

In a clear fresh water the tendency of brasses to dezincify is much reduced compared to seawater. Indeed it is only the uninhibited 60/40 types in stagnant or brackish water that are prone; *in*hibited 60/40 and *un*inhibited, 70/30 are usually satisfactory. It all depends on the actual state of the water. Generally the rate of corrosion on fresh water lakes and rivers is far, far less than in seawater.

COPPER AND NICKEL BASED ALLOYS

In Simple Terms . . .

The preceding discussion of the brasses and bronzes was but a scratch on the surface of the subject. There are a confusing number of different copper and nickel based alloys, both proprietory and standardized types as well as new ones continually being developed. But the most common ones that we boat owners come across are:

	Common uses
Copper	piping
Brass	fittings, screws (not recommended under water)
Manganese bronze	propellers and shafts (not recommended), deck fittings
Gunmetal	stern tubes, deck fittings
Aluminium bronze	seacocks
Silicon bronze	barb-ring nails
Monel	propeller shafts, seizing wire
Phosphor bronze	springs in snap-shackles
Aluminium brass	piping

Generally these metals are very corrosion resistant; the exceptions are brasses and manganese bronze which because of their zinc content tend to dezincify and crumble when immersed in seawater. So if possible avoid these materials for any application underwater. Copper and brass piping (but not so much aluminium brass) get eaten away by a fast water flow. Brass is susceptible to stress corrosion; tightened-up bolt heads tend to crack off in time. Brass and manganese bronze are best relegated to the interior of a boat or to deck fittings. Avoid using these materials underwater or even as fastenings in wood above the waterline, in places where they will be wetted frequently.

The other metals in the list can be used with confidence above and below the waterline. Inhibited aluminium brass is the best of the brasses with a low failure rate when used underwater.

From a corrosion point of view gunmetal, silicon bronze, aluminium bronze (and nickel-aluminium bronze) and Monel are excellent all-round metals. They are also strong (except gunmetal) so items made of gunmetal need to be of heavier section.

Copper has a reddish colour, brass a yellow colour. The low-zinc bronzes such as silicon bronze, aluminium bronze and gunmetal have a darker gold appearance (a bronze colour in fact). If in doubt about whether a bolt or other item is brass or bronze, put it alongside a freshly abraded piece of brass and something known to be bronze. The difference in colour is fairly evident, but for a precise opinion especially as to *which* bronze it is, a chemical analysis is essential. Monel can be mistaken for dull stainless steel as it has a silvery appearance like 'silver' coins.

Table 4
Nominal Compositions of the More Common Copper and Nickel-based Alloys

	% Copper	% Zinc	% Nickel	% Tin	% Aluminium	% Other metals	Remarks
Copper	99.9						Soft sheet or rivet: corrosion resistant
Copper-zinc alloys (brasses)							
70/30 Cartridge brass	70	30					Dezincifies under-water unless inhibited
60/40 Muntz metal (brass)	60	40					
Red brass	85	15					
Naval brass	60	39				1% Sn	Inhibited with tin
Admiralty brass	70	29				1% Sn + As	Inhibited. Good quality brass.
Aluminium brass	76	22			2	+ As	High tensile brass: the best brass.
Manganese bronze	58	39			1	0.25% Mn	High tensile brass. Dezincifies: really a brass.
Copper-tin alloys (bronzes)							
Tin bronze	88			5–10			Basic bronze
G bronze Admiralty gunmetal	88	2		10			Good material. Cast.
M bronze	88	4		6		+ Pb	Leaded gunmetal
Copper-based (zinc-free) alloys							
Silicon bronze	96					1½% or 3% Si	Very corrosion resistant
Aluminium bronze	88				9	3% Fe	Slight possibility of de-aluminification

COPPER AND NICKEL BASED ALLOYS

	% Copper	% Zinc	% Nickel	% Tin	% Aluminium	% Other metals	Remarks
Nickel-aluminium-bronze (NAB)	80		5		10	5% Fe	Slight tendency to stress corrosion in bolts
Nickel-aluminium-manganese bronze	75		2		8	+ 12% Mn	Super propeller material
Aluminium-silicon-bronze	91				6	2% Si	Corrosion resistant
Phosphor bronze	85–95			5–10		+ P	Springs
Copper-nickel alloys							
90/10 copper-nickel	90		10			1.5% Fe ⎫	Modern piping materials; good all-round corrosion resistance
70/30 copper-nickel	68		30			0.4% Fe ⎭	
*Hiduron	75		17		1.8	5% Mn	
Nickel bronze NB1	83		14.5		2.5		
Nickel-based alloys							
*Monel Alloy 400	32		66				Prop shafts
Monel Alloy K500	30		67		2.8		Stronger version of Monel 400
Monel Alloy 505 (S Monel)	30		66			+ 4% Si	Specialized Monel for high pressures and temperatures
*Inconel Alloy 625			60			22% Cr, 9% Mo ⎫	These super alloys are expensive but very strong and virtually inert in seawater. Some are also resistant at high temperatures
*Ni-O-nel Alloy 825 and *Incoloy	2		42			21% Cr, 30% Fe	
*Inconel Alloy 600			76			15% Cr, 7% Fe	
*Hastelloy alloys (many types), e.g. *Hastelloy C			54			16% Mo, 16% Cr ⎭	Wire rope has been made of Alloy 625. Alloy 825 is used for water-injected exhaust piping. Alloy C is completely resistant to pitting. Alloy 625 has high corrosion fatigue strength: used for wire rope and super-cavitating propellers.

Note: *trade names of a range of alloys

Chapter 3
Aluminium

Aluminium is a peculiar metal: on the one hand it can be a very corrosion resistant material because of its oxide skin; on the other it is low down on the galvanic scale and once corrosive action has pierced that skin it corrodes rapidly. In a way aluminium is similar to stainless steel, but because it is low on the galvanic scale almost all the other common marine metals corrode it severely when in electrical contact.

Pure aluminium is a weak metal and not much used. What we call 'aluminium' is in fact an alloy of aluminium containing small quantities of particular metals. These small ingredients have a profound effect on its strength and also on the corrosion resistance in seawater – quite unlike carbon steels, for example, which rust whatever their composition. Aluminium alloys are one-third the density of steel, stainless steel, brass, copper, etc and because of this are often referred to as 'light alloys' or 'light metal'.

Aluminium has been steadily used for hull construction for many years. Masts are now invariably of aluminium, as are window frames outboards and outdrives. It is also becoming quite popular for lightweight deck fittings.

Whenever aluminium is used where it can be wetted by seawater it *must* be of the correct grade. The alloys used ashore or in aircraft melt in seawater – quite literally. As with stainless steel, the different grades are only distinguished by numbers so it is necessary to talk in figures rather than more easily remembered names. First, a review of all the alloys currently manufactured before dealing specifically with the 'marine' alloys.

The British Standard categories are most commonly referred to in the UK. At the end of this chapter there is a table (Table 5) of equivalent alloys in the USA and other countries' specifications (to complicate matters some countries have a completely different numbering system). However, whatever specifying bodies decide, old numbers linger on for years and years, witness EN58J stainless steel.

In British Standards all aluminium alloys are divided into two divisions: 'wrought' (plate, bar, etc) and 'cast' (Table 6). The term cast is clear enough; wrought means that the metal during manufacture is literally forced into shape. Rolling produces plate, extrusion produces a section such as angle bar. Casting alloys are specified in BS 1490 and are numbered 0 to 30 and prefixed by LM. Thus we have LM10 for example. Another set of prefixes indicate the 'condition', i.e. whether the casting has been heat-treated or stress-relieved.

The wrought alloys are specified in British Standards 1470 to 1475 and numbered similarly to those in the USA. Each of the four digits comprising the number of the alloy defines the chemical composition and hence the properties. In addition, various degrees of 'temper' can be achieved by either heat treatment or work hardening.

Alloying Elements

Cast and wrought aluminium alloys are different because the former need good foundry characteristics. For instance the addition of silicon helps castability; it also improves strength. So does copper, and it is the aluminium-copper alloys, e.g. Duralumin or H15, that are strong, but these unfortunately have very low corrosion resistance. The alloys containing copper are commonly used in aircraft and must be avoided for marine work. Many early hulls of aluminium-copper failed catastrophically. Unfortunately, as with most metals strength does *not* go hand in hand with corrosion resistance; usually one advantage is gained at the expense of the other. Although aluminium alloys are available that are far stronger than mild steel, their corrosion resistance in seawater is too low to be useful. Consequently boat owners have to make do with other alloys that are half the strength of mild steel.

These are the aluminium-magnesium alloys and it is these that can be recommended for seawater use. Small quantities of magnesium and silicon play their role in strengthening the metal without significant detriment to its corrosion resistance. But any alloying element reduces the corrosion resistance from that of pure aluminium. Hence the well-known proprietary aluminium Alclad, which is a three-ply aluminium-copper type alloy with a very resistant pure aluminium coating on each side. Nevertheless Alclad is not to be recommended as a boatbuilding material.

Marine Grades

CASTINGS The particular British Standards and USA (AA) numbers which are of interest for their corrosion resistance are:

British Standards		USA (AA number) equivalent
LM5	5% Mg	514
LM6	12% Si	13
LM10	10% Mg	520
LM18	5% Si	443
LM25	7% Si 1% Mg	356

The cast alloys containing magnesium are very corrosion resistant, relatively strong and ductile, but are not so easily cast in the foundry as those alloys containing silicon. The 10% magnesium alloy requires a special treatment to prevent oxidation during casting, and can turn out to be porous. On the other hand, it is one of the toughest of all aluminium casting alloys. The aluminium-silicon alloys are not so strong but are easily cast and also corrosion resistant, though if anything a little less so than the magnesium ones. The major components of outboard motors are often die-cast in Alloy 13. LM25 is a good compromise between easy casting and fair strength. LM10 in particular has an attractive, clear surface film. As is so often the case, the best alloys (LM10 and LM5) are the ones that require the best foundry practice. Foundries producing castings in both aluminium and copper alloys have to be very careful to avoid getting copper contamination in the aluminium moulds because the presence of copper seriously affects corrosion resistance.

PLATE AND SECTION (WROUGHT) Whereas deck fittings are usually cast from the casting alloys, hulls and fuel tanks are made from the wrought alloys. Again those with copper content must be avoided for seawater use (Table 7). The alloys which *are* corrosion resistant are the aluminium-magnesium, aluminium-manganese and the aluminium-magnesium silicon and the aluminium silicon types. They are corrosion resistant roughly in that descending order with copper alloys coming well below the last. The Standards numbers group the various types of aluminium alloys into families as follows:

Alloy Element	Series
None	1000
Copper	2000
Manganese	3000
Magnesium	5000
Magnesium and silicon	6000
Zinc and magnesium	7000

The 'marine grades' are the 5000 and 6000 series. Most plate and sheet is made from the 5000 alloys; and most extrusions (tubes, bars etc) from the 6000 series because these alloys are easier to extrude. The 5000 series can be *work hardened* to increase their strength while the 6000 series can be *heat treated* again to increase their strength. However it must be remembered that extra strength is usually accompanied by a loss of ductility (elongation before fracture); in other words the metal becomes more brittle. Also during welding, for instance, the heat brings the strength local to the weld back down to or even below the original level of strength.

In the UK the most common marine alloys are 5083 and 6082, the former in plate form either in '0' condition (ie as manufactured), or in a 'quarter hard' form H116. Extrusions in 6082 often come in quite a high strength condition of T6, the highest of the tempers (T1-T6). See Table 6 on page 59.

53

Pitting Corrosion

The remarks in the rest of this chapter relate to the 'marine' grades that have been listed above. Aluminium has a tough protective oxide film which forms immediately bare metal is exposed to air or oxygen in water. It is this film that makes it generally corrosion resistant. Unpainted aluminium exposed to sea air soon pits and forms gritty 'molehills' all over its surface. This white gritty powder is unpleasant but very superficial and not harmful to the metal. In fact the action ceases after a time unless the powder is cleaned off at which it starts again. Immersed in seawater the same thing happens though the pits are rather larger, but shallow rather than deep and again not too harmful. In practice the underwater part of a hull will usually be antifouled but above water it can be left unpainted. The corrosion level is very low but the appearance suffers.

Paint on aluminium lasts longer than on steel; a scratch does not corrode and start to lift off the adjacent paint. A paint film also lasts longer than on wood, which tends to 'move' with variations in moisture content.

While pitting corrosion is not serious, two other forms of corrosion are, namely galvanic and poultice corrosion.

Galvanic Corrosion

Since aluminium is low down on the galvanic scale nearly all the common marine metals spell death to aluminium if brought into contact. All the copper alloys (brass, bronze, etc) cause severe attack in wet conditions, and even inside the cabin of a boat a white powdery corrosion will form around the heads of brass screws in an alloy fitting, for instance.

The situation with steel and Monel in contact with aluminium is not so bad. In mild circumstances, the cabin interior for example, direct contact is acceptable but in wet conditions, on deck or underwater, they must be insulated from one another.

The metals that *are* compatible are those that are close to aluminium on the galvanic scale (see Chapter 7) and those that have a protective oxide film. Since aluminium also has an oxide film the combination usually gives poor electrical contact and the corrosion is less than one would expect from their relative positions in the galvanic scale. Examples of such metals are stainless steel and chromium plate. In mild conditions there will be virtually no corrosion of the aluminium when it is in contact with stainless steel; in seawater or on deck there will be slight action. The same applies with chromium plate, but the chrome thickness should be generous with a good nickel coating underneath.

The metals that are close to aluminium on the galvanic scale are zinc and cadmium, so in practice one can use zinc or cadmium plated or galvanized fasteners in aluminium.

The different 'marine' grades of aluminium are all compatible with one another; the very slight difference on the galvanic scale of different alloys does not produce much reaction.

Even when relatively compatible metals like stainless steel, zinc and cadmium are used it is very advisable to insulate the joint if at all possible. The object is to *electrically* insulate the two metals so that a galvanic electric cell is less likely to be set up. This involves fitting a gasket between two mating surfaces – a gasket of neoprene or PVC is often used – and using non-conducting Tufnol washers and sleeves on bolts. Flexible sealant is not so reliable as a proper gasket because it can so easily be squeezed out to the point where contact is made on any small protrusions. This subject is described more fully in Chapter 7.

Suffice it to say here that aluminium is the one boat metal that requires careful protection from more noble metals and the best way to do this, if iron, copper, etc cannot be avoided, is to insulate thoroughly.

Before leaving this subject there are a few more important points to bear in mind. Copper, as I have said, is very corrosive to aluminium and so copper-based antifouling must never be used. Today there are antifoulings which are copper-free and entirely suitable for aluminium hulls. Water dripping off a copper or brass or bronze pipe onto aluminium will carry with it copper salts which again will cause serious corrosion. Mercury is another metal which is anathema to aluminium, so mercury-based antifouling paint must not be used, and if a thermometer is accidentally broken on board guard against the mercury running down into the bilges. Clean it all up as soon as possible.

55

While lead and aluminium are not as unhappy partners as copper, lead-based paint is to be avoided. Zinc chromate paint is the best type of paint to use.

Graphite is another killer and should not be used anywhere on aluminium: use a zinc-based grease instead, for instance on aluminium bolts. A dry aluminium thread will often cause a seized nut.

Do not clean aluminium with a steel wire brush because tiny bits of steel become embedded and later on cause nasty pitting. Use a bristle brush instead.

As usual, the corrosive activity in fresh water is much much less. Nevertheless it is still wise to insulate when attaching a copper alloy item to aluminium especially where moisture or rainwater is likely.

Poultice Corrosion

If a wet wick-like material is allowed to remain in contact with aluminium for a long time the metal forms copious amounts of a sticky white hydroxide which oozes out of the contact area. The volume of this corrosion product is quite alarming and can happen continually when wet wood is in contact with bare aluminium. Asbestos is another wick-like material that may be found in boats that can cause this type of action. Examples of situations where poultice corrosion can occur include aluminium frames and deck beams on a planked wooden hull, and aluminium fittings bolted to a wooden deck. The answer is to paint the aluminium with a zinc chromate primer. The wood should also be painted. An accumulation of dirt and fluff in the bilge of an aluminium hull can also cause this form of accelerated corrosion. Aluminium fasteners in wet wood are definitely not to be recommended.

Other Types of Corrosion

Stress corrosion of 'marine' aluminium is unlikely since these alloys are relatively weak. Rivets can lose their heads if they are not annealed first. If this is not done the rivetting process will leave a very high internal stress, and if seawater gets under the heads and the climate

ALUMINIUM

is tropical. . . . However this combination of circumstances does not often arise. Welded joints do not have this problem. Rivets with magnesium content of less than 3.5% are less susceptible to stress corrosion, eg 5754. Clinch bolts, Huck bolts, blind rivets etc should be 7075 anodised to at least 15 microns.

Anodising

This treatment successfully stops the pitting and roughening of bare aluminium. It is commonly used on masts and deck fittings and providing the coating is not chafed off, corrosion is virtually eliminated. It is not proof against galvanic action, though, so fittings made of more noble metals should still be insulated from the aluminium.

Anodising is produced by an electrolytic process whereby the aluminium is made the anode and deliberately 'corroded'. This forms a positive film of oxide which is very adherent. It can also be coloured. The process is quite inexpensive and well worth while on any aluminium where painting is inappropriate. It also lasts longer than paint. Flapping halyards or an unfair halyard lead will gradually wear away the anodising and expose the metal, so a little care in checking against chafe is well worth while.

The relevant British Standard is BS 1615. The protection given to the metal depends largely on the thickness of the oxide film and according to this standard should be Grade AA25, for marine work, the thickest grade mentioned. Thinner grades, e.g. AA20 or AA15, are only suitable for clean inland conditions or indoors. Hence caravan window frames will be satisfactory for a boat on inland fresh waters but not at sea. It is mandatory under BS 1615 that after anodising the surface is 'sealed', which is another chemical process that adds to corrosion resistance.

The Standard also mentions that the life of the coating depends, apart from thickness, on the frequency of washing to remove dirt and deposits. Hence the advice to wash down with fresh water and wax-polish a mast, say once a year.

THE METALS THEMSELVES

In Conclusion

Always use the marine grade alloys such as 5083, 6082. Avoid attaching anything made of brass, copper or bronze to aluminium: if it has to be done, thoroughly insulate the joint. Use stainless steel fastenings. Avoid paints containing lead, mercury or copper. Bare aluminium of marine grade stands up to the sea very well, but for the sake of appearance it ought to be anodised or painted.

Table 5
Approximately Equivalent Aluminium Alloys

USA	France	Germany	United Kingdom	International
5083	5083	AlMg4.5Mn	5083	AlMg4.5Mn
5086	5086	AlMg4Mn		AlMg4
5454	5454	AlMg2.7Mn	5454	AlMg3Mn
	5754	AlMg3		AlMg3
	6005A	AlMgSi0,7		AlSiMg
6063	6060	AlMgSi0,5	6063	AlMgSi
6061	6061	AlMg1SiCu	6061	AlMg1SiCu
	6082	AlMgSi1	6082	AlSi1Mg

ALUMINIUM

Table 6
Properties

Alloy	Temper	Resistance to marine corrosion	Suitability for anodizing	
			Protection	Hard anodizing
5083	0 and H111	A	A	A
	H116	A	A	A
5086	0 and H111	A	A	A
	H116	A	A	A
5454	H111	A	A	A
5754	0 and H111	A	A	A
	H24	A	A	A
6060	T5	A	A	A
6005A	T5	A	A	A
6061	T6	A	A	A
6082	T6	A	A	A
6106	T5	A	A	A

A = very good

Alloy	Temper	Tensile characteristics			Elastic modulus (MPa)
		UTS MPa	0.2 % PS MPa	Elongation %	
5083	0 and H111	305	170	22	71000
	H116	340	250	15	71000
5086	0 and H111	280	150	23	71000
	H116	320	230	16	71000
5454	H111	260	180	22	70000
5754	0 and H111	220	130	25	70000
	H24	260	205	20	70000
6005A	T5	300	285	13	69500
6060	T5	220	195	11	69500
6061	T6	305	270	13	69500
6082	T6	315	280	12	69500
6106	T5	250	200	10	69500

MEAN MECHANICAL CHARACTERISTICS AT 20°C

Table 7

Comparisons of Widely Used Marine Aluminium Alloys to BS and AA Standards (% composition)

	Si	Fe	Cu	Mn	Mg	Cr	Ni	Zn
BS 5083	0.4	0.4	0.1	0.4–1.0	4.0–4.9	0.05–0.25	–	0.25
AA 5083	0.4	0.4	0.1	0.3–1.0	4.0–4.9	0.05–0.25	–	0.25
AA 5086	0.4	0.5	0.1	0.2–0.7	3.5–4.5	0.05–0.25	–	0.25
AA 6082	0.7–1.3	0.5	0.1	0.4–1.0	0.5–1.2	0.25	–	0.2
AA 6061	0.4–0.8	0.7	0.15–0.4	0.15	0.8–1.2	0.04–0.35	–	0.25

For comparison again, here is a non-marine copper alloy of the Duralumin type:

	Si	Fe	Cu	Mn	Mg	Cr	Ni	Zn
2014	0.5–1.2	1.0	3.9–5.0	0.4–1.2	0.2–0.8	0.1	–	0.25

Very small amounts of alloying elements radically change the strength and corrosion resistance of aluminium.

Chapter 4
Steel and Iron

In terms of corrosion there is not much to say about steel and iron: only that they rust. All of the many different types of carbon and low-alloy steels and irons corrode away at much the same rate in seawater. If it were not for the fact that steel and iron are by far the cheapest metals they would be unacceptable for marine use. Therefore much effort has been spent on coatings to reduce this amount of corrosion; paints, metallic coatings, etc. Fortunately these measures can be very effective.

Steel

Steels can be broadly categorized as follows, and their compositions are shown in Table 8.

PLAIN CARBON STEEL—MILD STEEL. Steels to which no additions have been made other than small amounts necessary to achieve a good material. Variation of the very small carbon content alters its strength and its uses. The most commonly used structural carbon steel is loosely called 'mild steel', which is a term that came into use to denote a steel that was not brittle, brittleness having caused many fractures in the early days of steel shipbuilding. Mild steel is very ductile (stretchable) and the word 'mild' is a good indication of its nature: it has no hasty vices. Ships large and small are made of mild steel. (The 'iron deck' beloved of fiction authors is rubbish: wrought iron was only used in shipbuilding for a relatively brief period in the last century.) Mild steel is also used for steel boats, hence the corrosion lessons learned in the ship world are directly applicable to boats, and so are the paints.

THE METALS THEMSELVES

HIGH STRENGTH LOW-ALLOY STEELS. These are steels with small quantities of manganese, chromium, copper or nickel to give higher strength. The corrosion resistance in seawater is not enhanced. Cor-Ten is one well known low-alloy steel having about 0.5% copper and 0.6% chromium. In marine *atmospheres*, though, the rate of rusting is much reduced – a point to be discussed later.

HIGH STRENGTH AND SPECIAL STEELS. Steel can be made several times stronger than mild steel by small additions of chromium, molybdenum, nickel and manganese. The percentages are small, up to 3% or so, and the effect on the rate of rusting is quite small. Included in this category are such special steels as ball-race steels, spring steels, 'high strength' and 'ultra high strength' steels.

In between the low-alloy and stainless steels there are groups of steels that have 10% or so of alloying elements, e.g. the heat-resisting steels.

It is the carbon and low-alloy steels that are mostly used in hull construction and boat fittings, and the corrosion resistance of all the types within these two groups is much the same. Investigations into possible variations in composition within the ranges practical for large-scale use has shown that the corrosion resistance varies but little.

Rust is the corrosion product resulting from an electrochemical action. For various reasons (mill scale, for example) electric potential differences occur over the surface of a steel plate, thus setting up numerous galvanic cells, in effect miniature batteries. The iron goes into solution as iron hydroxide which is then oxidized by oxygen in the water into yellow-red hydrated ferric oxide, known as rust. Water (or any liquid that conducts electricity) and oxygen are vital ingredients to this corrosion cell. Absence of either nullifies rusting. Hence the success of dehumidifiers and also the fact that rusting is almost stopped in stagnant water where the oxygen supply is limited. The rate of rusting increases with the acidity of the water and conversely reduces with alkalinity. Seawater is a neutral solution, neither acid nor alkaline. Alkaline conditions are created in contact with cement and under cathodic protection.

Corrosion Rates in Seawater

All carbon and low-alloy steels corrode at much the same rate in seawater, but what in fact is the rate? Unprotected, steel rusts away quietly at the rate of about 5 mils per year (125 μm) when submerged in seawater, so theoretically 1/8 in. (3 mm) thick hull plating will last 24 years. This assumes that corrosion takes place on only *one* side of the plate, and that the rate of attack is not accelerated by galvanic or bacterial action nor slowed by a paint scheme or cathodic protection or the absence of oxygen.

The corrosion rate increases considerably when the steel is not fully immersed but is continually wetted, as in the area between wind and water (7). Here oxygen is amply provided to hasten the oxidization process. Embedded in clean mud the rate drops off

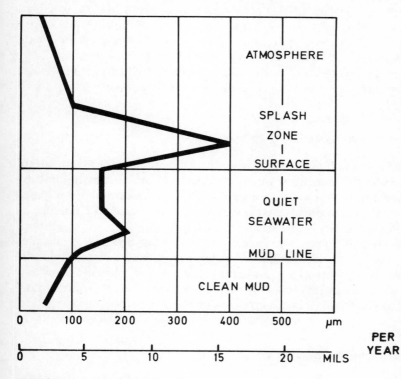

(7) Corrosion rates of bare mild steel.

because less oxygen is available and because the rusted layer is undisturbed and acts as a protective barrier.

A flow of water encourages rusting of bare steel. At 2 knots the rate is three times as much, at 4 knots five times as much. Whereas a water flow hardens the protective film on stainless steels, with carbon steels the rust product is washed away exposing new metal which in turn starts to rust.

Steel plates and bars are made by a hot-rolling process which causes the surface to be covered with a mill scale of iron oxides. If this mill scale is not removed, whether the steel is painted or left bare the plate will be prone to pit badly. This is because the mill scale is more noble (by about 0.3 volts) than the underlying steel and consequently local cells are set up with the steel being eaten away where it is exposed. Another factor is that the mill scale is brittle and when it flakes off it carries any paint with it. So whether the steel is left bare or painted (or protected in any way), it is essential to remove the mill scale, done by weathering or hand cleaning or shot-blasting. This subject is mentioned in Chapter 12 on Metal Hulls. The rate of pitting of bare steel with the mill scale left on is about 30 mils per year (0.75 mm) in seawater.

Galvanic Corrosion

Like aluminium, steel is low in the galvanic series and will suffer accelerated corrosion when in electrical contact with the brasses and bronzes in water. Hence the need for insulation from these metals unless the area ratio is the right way round, for instance a bronze seacock on a steel hull (see Chapter 7).

Weld metal has been found to have virtually no adverse galvanic effect on the adjacent parent metal, or vice-versa. But rusting will invariably start first at a weld because unless it is ground flush the paint film thickness will fluctuate over the relatively rough weld. The roughness of the weld 'shows through'.

Impingement Attack

Where a jet of water impinges on steel ('steel' including cast iron)

A dezincified manganese bronze propeller. The tips of the blades are crumbling away. Manganese bronze is not actually a bronze but a brass and as such is very liable to dezincify in seawater. (MG Duff International Ltd)

Copper bolts which once held a stainless steel fitting in place. The stainless has galvanically attacked the bolts near their heads. (MG Duff International Ltd)

Three different types of coated fasteners after five years' exposure to a marine atmosphere. Top electroplated, middle hot-dip galvanized, bottom sherardized. (Galvanised Bolts & Nuts Ltd)

Pitting and crevice corrosion on stainless steel components, a nut and two screws. Screws and bolts in wet wood are particularly vulnerable.

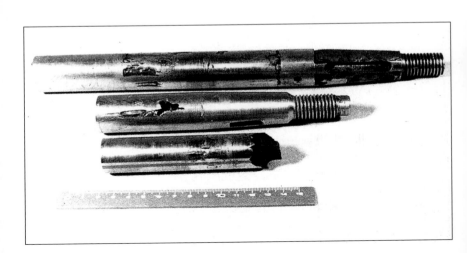

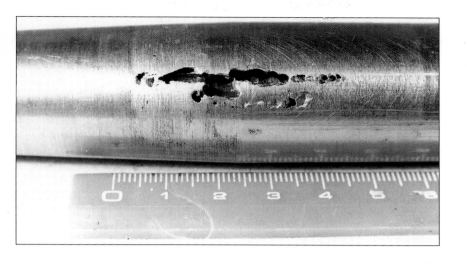

Stainless steel propeller shafts that have suffered from crevice corrosion in way of the bearing or the propeller. From a corrosion point of view stainless is far from ideal for the inactive yacht moored in salt water. (MG Duff International Ltd)

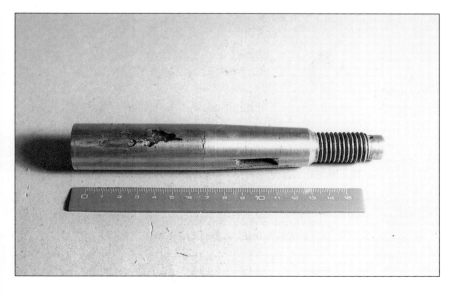

Wasted steel floor bolts. Note that without withdrawing the bolts one might be led to believe they were sound. (MG Duff International Ltd)

A drain port cut in the bulwark of a steel fishing boat in the course of construction. The small lip thus formed is a water trap. The rough gas-cut edge of the plate is another rust-raiser.

Shroud attachments on a metal boat are simple to arrange. To obviate fatigue and the possibility of a poor area of weld the plate needs to be massive – rather more massive than on this aluminium boat.

Neglect can cause more corrosion than everything else put together. This boat was, once upon a time, someone's pride and joy.

A copper-bottomed investment! In this case very thin copper nickel sheet has been glued to the underside of the GRP hull.

Massive rusting has forced this steel keel bar off the keel. Perhaps it was never hot-dip galvanized nor painted and bedded into place.

Trouble brewing: are the rust streaks coming from the cast iron keel or the keel bolts?

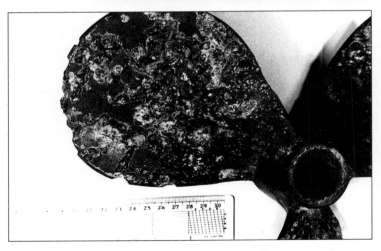

The result of gross electrolytic action from stray currents. This is an aluminium boat with aluminium shaft strut. It was moored for a few months alongside a steel pontoon and a steel boat on which electric welding was being carried out. The aluminium suffered deep pitting and large areas of paint were lifted off.

Moth-eaten effect caused by the dezincification of manganese bronze. If the metal appears bright immediately after it is taken from the water, suspect electrolysis. (Eric Coltham, *Motor Boat and Yachting*) the rate of corrosion is greatly increased. The effect of velocities of 2 and 4 knots has been mentioned, but in the case of a water-injected exhaust bend for example, the impingement velocity can be much higher. The corrosion rate gradually increases as water veolcity increases. At extreme speeds like 80 knots, or in engineering terms 135 ft/sec (41 m/sec), a jet of seawater can corrode right through a $\frac{1}{4}$ in. (6 mm) thick steel plate in about nine months. The problem of exhaust injection is mentioned in Chapter 13 on Engine Corrosion.

Steel is not susceptible to hydrogen embrittlement or stress corrosion cracking except the very high strength steels with yield strengths of over 70 tons/sq in. On the other hand, steel has a low corrosion fatigue resistance in seawater so the situation where there is engine or propeller vibration causing continual flexing of a steel part which is also wet or wetted with seawater needs careful design; the shell plating over propellers, and chainplates of mild steel flat bar, are two examples.

Galvanizing, or to a much lesser degree electroplating has a very beneficial effect in terms of corrosion fatigue. Not only does the coating give a physical barrier between the steel and the water but it gives cathodic protection. Any minute pores or cracks in the coating allowing seawater to get at the steel are automatically sealed up by a zinc deposit. Bare steel wire rope which is continually being flexed lasts no time at all in seawater, but when galvanized its life is extended to a useful period. Not that anyone would use bare steel wire rope, but it shows how effective the zinc coating is. To take a more practical example, chainplates made of flat bar ought to be galvanized.

Sulphate-Reducing Bacteria

Oddly enough, steel can be corroded by the action of organisms, close to a muddy bottom or in the top layers of mud and especially in polluted water (8). These bacteria use sulphates present in the muddy water as part of their metabolism and allow the oxygen in the seawater to be made available for the corrosion process where otherwise none would be present. Accelerated attack is the result. Steel boats lying on mud berths in polluted waters are prone to this

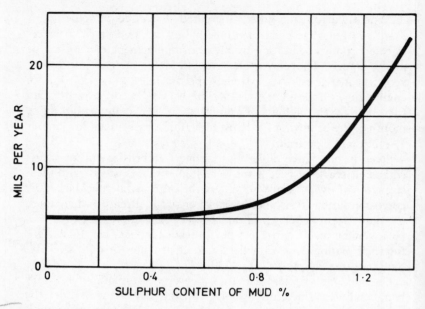

(8) The effect of sulphides in mud on the corrosion rate of bare mild steel. Sulphides cause accelerated attack on steel hulls of boats moored on mud berths, where the paint has been scaped off. The mud in polluted industrial ports can have a sulphur content of 1–2% or even more.

sort of attack where the paint has been damaged.

Oak is liable to accelerate the corrosion of steel and iron where it is in contact: the 'tannins' of the wood attack the metal. Oak is the one wood that has a deleterious effect. On the other hand cement is positively advantageous, as ferrocement hull constructors and of course civil engineers know very well. A thin (2–3 mm) cover of highly alkaline cement mortar with a paint scheme adequately protects bare mild steel against seawater: hence ferrocement hulls, cast-in concrete ballast in steel hulls, and 'cement wash' for tanks in steel hulls.

Corrosion in a Marine Atmosphere

In clean *salt-free* air, rusting of bare steel is hardly serious; in dry climates rusting is negligible. It is salt air and humid conditions that cause a rate of rusting almost as much as that of steel immersed in salt water. Remove the damp by dehumidification and rusting ceases. Add wet salt and heat and the rate of rusting can reach 0.05 inches per year (1 mm), as on tropical coasts.

Immersed, the various carbon and low-alloy steels rust at much the same rate, but in contrast the exact composition of the steel has a great influence on the corrosion rate in the atmosphere. The low-alloy steels suffer a third or less of the attack shown by mild steel. They still rust, of course, and are best called 'slow-rusting' steels. The phenomenon is caused by a more tenacious and less permeable layer of rust compared to that formed by mild steel. Cor-Ten is one commercial low-alloy steel that exhibits this property.

Cor-Ten Steel

This is a low-alloy steel that is much used as a structural steel for buildings and bridges. For this use it is often left unprotected, and although it rusts it does so uniformly and the action virtually stops after a year or two. No maintenance is therefore required.

Cor-Ten is also used in hull construction for small craft, especially in America. It has two advantages, namely slightly greater yield strength and a lower rate of rusting in a marine atmosphere, though it costs more than mild steel. (Cor-Ten is discussed further in Chapter 12.)

Cor-Ten has small additions of copper, chromium and nickel which give it its properties. Low-alloy steels tend to be slightly more noble than mild steel so they will be very slightly protected underwater, for instance if the propeller shaft is a low-alloy steel on a mild steel boat; but the difference in potential is not nearly enough to stop rusting.

Iron

At this point it is worth delving into the definitions and differences between steel, cast iron and wrought iron. There is a whole host of iron alloys (i.e. irons and steels), each produced from the ore by varying degrees of refinement at the furnace. Pig iron is the crudest product, containing many impurities including up to 4% carbon and 4% of other elements, and is very brittle. Purified by degrees, the pig iron is converted into more usable iron and hence into steel. A steel is an alloy of iron and carbon, but in contrast to iron the carbon is fully dissolved and is a very small percentage – less than 1.7%. Cast iron has more than 1.7% carbon.

In the early days of steelmaking the purification of pig iron was achieved by oxidizing the impurities including carbon with iron oxide in the furnace, producing a pure iron mixed with slag called wrought iron which contained only 0.03%C. Wrought iron is stronger in tension than cast iron and so was a much more useful material for ships and bridges, et al. However the development of steel soon ousted wrought iron because even the early steels were much more uniform, and stronger and more ductile than wrought iron.

While wrought iron is not much used today, cast iron is still popular. The various grades of cast iron are produced by varying the composition (and here carbon is important) and by varying the crystalline structure as seen under a microscope. The latter is done by various furnace procedures. Hence one sees names such as 'grey iron' and 'white iron', so called because of the appearance of a fracture. Grey iron is basic cast iron and under BS 1452 there are various grades with tensile strengths ranging from 10 T/sq. in. (150 N/mm^2) to 27 T/sq. in. (400 N/mm^2). Then there is nodular cast iron with greater strength (BS 2789), 'nodular' meaning that the carbon in the iron is held in compact graphite nodules rather than flakes as in cast grey iron. Nodular cast iron is also called SG iron, the SG standing for spheroidal graphite. Other names for it are ductile iron, nodular graphite iron, and spherultic iron. Nodular cast iron is a steel-like metal easily machined and giving a smooth finish. It is the most modern development of cast iron; previously the only reasonably ductile cast iron available was 'malleable iron'.

Malleable iron is a white iron which has been heat-treated to reduce brittleness. There are three groups, whiteheart, blackheart and pearlite (BS 309, 310 and 333 respectively). These terms refer to the process by which they are made and their resulting crystal structure.

More sophisticated irons include the nickel cast irons and the high-alloy cast irons, both having enhanced strength and ductility.

The corrosion rate of iron in seawater is much the same as that of mild steel, but the form of corrosion is very different. Whereas mild steel gradually wastes away and becomes physically smaller, iron tends to retain its shape and outward size but rots away from inside. Superficially it may look sound, but a sharp prod can reveal massive corrosion underneath. This form of attack is called graphitization because a graphite residue is all that is left.

The ordinary cast irons have a poor resistance to shock and fracture fairly easily; they are also readily attacked by sulphate-reducing bacteria.

Ductile iron is the modern equivalent of cast iron. It does not fracture as easily but its corrosion resistance is much the same. Nickel cast iron with 1–3% of nickel is a finer-grained iron but again the corrosion resistance is barely enhanced.

There are families of high-alloy cast iron: irons with large amounts of chromium, or nickel or silicon. The austenitic nickel cast irons have a low uniform rate of corrosion in seawater and do not suffer from graphitization; they rust but slowly on deck. These cast irons are often called Ni-Resist, but this name is actually a trademark. The high-silicon cast irons (about 14% Si) also have a much enhanced resistance to corrosion, as do the high-chromium irons (12–35% Cr). (See Tables 8 and 9.)

Unless a high-alloy cast iron is used, with much increased cost, the various 'cheap and cheerful' cast irons corrode at much the same rate as carbon and low-alloy steels.

WROUGHT IRON. Wrought iron has the reputation of resisting corrosion and some of the old wrought iron ships did last a long time – witness the *Great Britain* now preserved at Bristol. The old iron ships had to be made of thicker plate under Lloyds Rules because even the best wrought iron had a tensile strength of only 21 T/sq. in. as against mild steel at 30 T/sq. in. There was therefore more thickness to rust away in the iron plating.

There is no direct technical evidence from controlled experiments that wrought iron is significantly better than mild steel in seawater, but in the atmosphere some grades such as Staffordshire are more resistant, in the same way as Cor-Ten steel. Since it is not much used nowadays corrosion studies are few and far between.

Wrought iron is relatively pure; the greatest concentration is up to 1% slag which during the manufacturing process is elongated by rolling, causing fibres which give the metal a grain rather like wood. Wooden boats often used to have wrought iron brackets under the gunwales and thwarts and inspection of an old boat often reveal these to be thoroughly rotten.

Incidentally manufacturers of 'wrought iron' gates etc do not use wrought iron any longer; they use pieces of mild steel flat bar tack-welded together.

Coatings to Protect Steels and Irons

There are numerous ways of reducing or eliminating rusting:

> Paint
> Galvanizing
> Zinc or cadmium electroplating
> Zinc or aluminium spraying
> Sherardizing
> Chinese galvanizing
> Tin or lead coating
> Nickel-chromium plating
> Nylon dipping
> Sheathing with fibreglass
> Cladding with sheet metal
> Weld cladding

Taking these in order, paint as a subject is discussed fully in Chapter 12 on Metal Hulls.

Zinc, Cadmium and Aluminium Coatings

As zinc, cadmium and aluminium are less noble than steel, a coating of zinc or cadmium cathodically (i.e. sacrificially) protects the underlying steel. Scratches are self-healing; when wetted, a small cell is set up and the surrounding zinc is deposited onto the bare steel until it is covered. On large areas of galavanized surface the scratch can be up to about $\frac{3}{16}$ in. (5 mm) wide and still receive cathodic protection.

Various processes are used to 'stick' the coating onto the steel or iron. Galvanizing is a common process whereby the item is dipped into molten zinc, which can also be electroplated on, or alternatively sprayed in place. Sherardizing is another method of applying zinc. Cadmium is usually deposited by electroplating, while aluminium (rarely used) is sprayed on.

The effectiveness, i.e. the life, of a metal coating depends largely on its thickness, and this is where hot-dip galvanizing scores because the zinc coat thickness achieved is far greater than by the other processes – except spraying, where again a good thickness can be built up so long as adhesion can be maintained and porosity minimized. Hot-dip galvanizing produces a coating thickness of at least 2 mils (50 μm) and probably 3 or 4 mils, whereas sherardizing and plating only give $1\frac{1}{2}$ mil (38 μm) at the most. The life of galvanizing will therefore be much longer than that of electroplating or sherardizing.

The relative merits of the three coating metals, zinc, cadmium and aluminium, become insignificant in relation to the effect of the thickness of the coating. Cadmium is said to be slightly more effective in a marine atmosphere, but since it can only be electroplated on as a thin coating this advantage is immaterial. Hence there is rarely a good case for cadmium rather than zinc protection. Cadmium has much the same colour and texture as zinc plating or galvanizing.

Aluminium sprayed coatings are as good as zinc, thickness for thickness, when exposed to a marine atmosphere and considerably better when fully immersed. The coating should be pure aluminium rather than an alloy. Adhesion of the aluminium spray is of paramount importance and the steel must first be grit-blasted. Aluminium spraying is a technique that is rarely used in the boat world but would seem to have distinct possibilities for steel hulls.

The basic problem with spraying is that the coating is generally very porous compared to plating or hot-dipping. Consequently a thick coating is essential, provided that adhesion can be maintained.

Zinc rather than aluminium spraying is more common, but again not as common as galvanizing. It requires good preparation by shot-blasting and skilled operators to minimize porosity and ensure an even coating. As with paint, it is difficult to achieve an even coating especially on sharp edges and joins. An unpainted zinc-sprayed coating, like other bare zinc coatings, does not last long underwater. An even thicker coating than galvanizing can be achieved with spraying 4 to 8 mils (100–200 μm).

Many of these processes are covered by ISO or British Standards:

BS 729	Hot-dip galvanizing after fabrication	ISO 1459–61
BS 1706	Electroplating (zinc and cadmium)	ISO 2081–2
BS 4921	Sherardizing	
BS 2569	Sprayed aluminium and zinc	ISO 2063
BS 3382	Zinc-plated nuts and bolts	

Since hot-dip galvanizing is generally the most satisfactory method it is worth discussing in more detail. BS 729 specifies a *minimum* coating weight of 305–610 g/m^2 for steel items depending on the size of the item, 610 g/m^2 for iron castings, and 305 g/m^2 for threaded work which in the process is spun to 'clean' the thread. These awkward metric figures originate from the old Imperial coating of 1 oz/sq ft (= 305 g/m^2) which in turn is equivalent to a thickness of 1.7 mils (= 43 μm). Extra clearance must be given on threads to allow for the coating thickness. With nuts and bolts, the bolt is threaded normally and galvanized while the nut is tapped 0.02 in. (0.4 mm) oversize *after* galvanizing. The bare steel thread on the nut is then protected by the zinc on the bolt thread.

A roughened surface, caused by shot-blasting for instance, will give a thicker coating. If a really thick coat is required this is a more effective method than double dipping. Before galvanizing the article must be clean and free of paint or grease, but light rust does not matter; it is also acid pickled. If the steel has not been cleaned sufficiently a bare area will result. There are numerous small galvanizing plants around the country and the process is generally quite inexpensive, but for all exterior or underwater items it is vital to state that *hot-dip* galvanizing is required, otherwise electro-galvanizing (another common term for electroplating) might be employed resulting in a very thin coat of zinc. Ideally ask for 'hot-dip galvanizing to BS 729' or an equivalent national standard.

Any article to be galvanized should not have sealed voids, for instance a length of tube should not be sealed at either end, because of the possibility of an explosion when it is dipped in the hot molten zinc. A hole should be drilled at each end. Galvanizing does not affect the strength of structural steels.

Electroplating steel to BS 1706 involved asking for one of three coating thicknesses. For marine work Class A should be used (the thickest), which will give a minimum of 0.6 mils (15 μm) for cadmium and 1.5 mils (38 μm) for zinc. Again, *zinc* plating is preferable to cadmium. If something is merely 'commercially plated' rather than to this standard very thin coatings may be given which are quite useless for marine work even inside the cabin.

The British Standard for sherardizing has two classes of thicknesses, Class 1 at 1.2 mils (30 μm) and Class 2 at half that thickness. A sprayed coating to BS 2569 Part 1 should have an average thickness of 4 mils (100 μm). In the sherardizing process the item is put in a sealed container together with a quantity of zinc dust and heated to a controlled temperature. A uniform coating is obtained which is very resistant to knocks. No etch-priming is required when painting.

Clearly it pays to specify a coating to a standard and not just to ask for 'galvanizing' or 'plating'.

How does zinc perform in seawater? The corrosion rate of a zinc coating does not vary much according to how it was applied so long as adhesion is good. In static seawater a bare galvanized coating wastes away at about 1 mil per year (25 μm) so even a thick coating of $3\frac{1}{2}$ mil (86 μm) will only last three to four years. Polluted seawater and mud containing hydrogen sulphide corrodes bare zinc at an accelerated rate.

Zinc also corrodes away much faster as the water starts to move. At 2 knots the rate is 3 mils per year (75 μm). Consequently, on immersed surfaces it is essential to paint the coating. As long as the paint is 'keyed' to the zinc (with an etch-primer for example) galvanizing will last a very long time, and the underlying steel will be completely protected.

On deck, a heavy galvanized coating (e.g. to BS 729) will last many years – over ten and perhaps more, even unprotected. The rate of corrosion is about five to eight years per mil. Painted, the coating life is extended several times. A painted electroplated surface will also last a long time on deck providing the electroplating is to a good thickness, e.g. BS 1706 Class A. Bare thin electroplating will start to rust through in no time on deck.

A zinc, aluminium or cadmium coating creates a very sound base for painting – far sounder than bare steel – but it is essential to free the surface of grease and preferably to use an etch-primer. A galvanized surface in damp conditions (rather than fully immersed or fully open to the wind and rain) can develop 'white rust', a voluminous white powder. Painting can prevent this, but good adhesion of the paint is very important. The greasy galvanizing flux must be neutralized with an etch-primer before the normal primer and top coats are applied.

Galvanizing and metal spraying are discussed again in Chapter 12.

CHINESE GALVANIZING. Worth mentioning, this is a process whereby the item is heated to red heat and plunged into boiling pitch. The pitch is absorbed into the 'pores' of the steel or iron and creates a better protective film than a bituminous paint applied cold. The type of pitch to use is that obtained from roofing contractors or building merchants. When dipping the red hot item beware of fumes and flames. This practice of dipping items used to be commonly used for chandlery on fishing boats; it is also known as Swedish galvanizing. It is said to be effective for a few years but is no substitute for hot-dip galvanizing.

Tin, Lead, Nickel and Chromium Plating

Unlike zinc, aluminium and cadmium, these coatings are *more* noble than steel and consequently as soon as the coating is scratched through the underlying steel will be preferentially corroded and rust badly. In principle these coatings are not suitable for marine work: they can only successfully be used where the coating itself has a low rate of corrosion and also forms a complete watertight barrier.

Tin itself (and lead too) corrode very slowly in seawater and it has been found that painted tinned steel lasts a long time, providing it is not scratched. Nevertheless it is rarely used in the boat world. Tin is very close to steel in the galvanic series and under oxygen starved conditions their relative positions in the series can change over so that the tin coating protects the steel: hence the success of 'tinned' food.

Occasionally petrol (gasoline) tanks are made of tin or lead coated steel called Terne plate which makes a reasonably corrosion-free (on the inside anyway) fuel tank.

Nickel and chromium coatings were described in Chapter 2 on Brasses and Bronzes. In general nickel (or chromium on nickel) coatings on a steel or iron item are a waste of money for marine work, and even when done to BS 1224 Grade IS will not give as good or as economic a service as painted hot-dip galvanizing under-water. On deck, although protection will be given for many years (unless the coating is scratched) the appearance will deteriorate rapidly.

Nylon Dipping

A relatively new method of protection, this gives good service provided that the whole item is encased and also that the coating is not chafed through. Unfortunately both these requirements are difficult to meet.

Sheathing with Fibreglass

Much the same comments apply to sheathing as to nylon dipping. Steel hulls are very rarely sheathed with fibreglass as is sometimes done to wooden hulls, but steel propeller shafts are sometimes wrapped in it. It is essential to clean and abrade the steel first, and of course a problem occurs at the end of the sleeve thus formed: how to stop rust creeping between the covering fibreglass and the shaft. With this method there is still the layer of shaft within the bearing to protect and sometimes a metal spray (e.g. Monel) or weld coating or a shrunk-on bronze sleeve is employed.

Cladding

Recently techniques have been developed that allow a metal cladding to be put on steel. The cladding can be in the form of sheet spot-welded in place, or thin sheet bonded at the mill. It is usually of a highly corrosion resistant metal like copper-nickel, stainless steel or Monel. Weld cladding is another recent development that at the moment is the only type of cladding used in the boat world, for instance for building up worn propeller shafts with identical metal to the parent metal. The process involves spirally welding a layer onto the shaft and then machining down to the required diameter. It is a very successful technique and can also be used to build up a coating of stainless steel, Monel or copper-nickel, subsequently machined off, to provide a hard and corrosion resistant bearing surface.

In Fresh Waters

In clean fresh water the rate of corrosion of steel and iron is much reduced and the degree of protection to avoid rusting is far less critical. The actual rate of corrosion depends on such things as the oxygen content of the water; stagnant water will have little and will therefore be less corrosive. Other factors are the acidity, the mineral quality and the flow, if any. While hot-dip galvanizing is still well worth while, electroplating to BS 1706 Class A (to gain a reasonable thickness) is long-lasting on deck but ought to be painted below the water. In polluted and muddy waters the attack can be much more severe, but of course on deck the same 'clean and fresh' conditions may apply. In polluted atmospheres the rate of attack again increases as the following table shows.

The life of the unpainted coating to first sign of rusting is given in years. Each coating tested was 1 mil (25 μm) thick.

Atmosphere	Cadmium Plated	Zinc Plated
Devon coast	2–3	2
Devon inland	8–15	5
Urban average	2–3	3–4
Industrial Birmingham	1–1$\frac{1}{2}$	2–3

A zinc-coated hull in fresh water will last a very long time indeed, especially in 'hard' rather than 'soft' water because a deposit forms on the zinc giving a protective scale which in turn reduces the rate of corrosion.

To Conclude

Common mild steel and cast iron are excellent materials in many ways; they are strong and economical – but they rust. But at least the rusting is obvious and gradual and the metal is unlikely to fail suddenly as can happen to stainless steel or high strength metals. Some low-alloy steels like Cor-Ten are 'slow rusting' in a marine *atmosphere* but rust much like mild steel when immersed in seawater.

All steels should have the mill scale removed before painting.

Hot-dip zinc galvanizing is generally far superior and more 'cost effective' than zinc or cadmium electroplating. To get the best galvanizing ask for the work to be done to a standard, e.g. BS 729. If the galvanized item is to be immersed it is essential to paint it, preferably by using a self-etch primer for the first coat. Galvanizing gives a tough self-healing coating and one which is quite inexpensive.

Electroplating is a waste of time unless a standard is specified, e.g. BS 1706 Class A. Zinc electric plating is preferable to cadmium because the coating thickness is greater. Nevertheless hot-dip galvanizing will give a much longer life and yet its cost is only very slightly more than electroplating.

Galvanized or plated steel makes a good base for paint which in turn gives a long life to the paint *and* the metal coating providing the paint is 'keyed' to the coat.

THE METALS THEMSELVES

Table 8

Nominal % Compositions of the Different Types of Iron

	Carbon	Silicon	Nickel	Copper	Chromium
Grey cast iron	4	3	—	—	—
Ductile, nodular or spheroidal cast iron	4	3	2.5	—	—
Malleable cast iron	2.65	1.65	—	—	—
High-silicon cast iron	0.85	14.5	—	—	—
High-chromium cast iron	4	3	5	3	12–35
Austenitic Ni-Resist: various types 1–6	3	1.6	13.5–36	0–7.5	0–5.5

Balance is iron.

Chapter 5
Miscellaneous Metals

Lead and Solder

A very dense, low melting-point metal with a high resistance to corrosion, lead is consequently an excellent material for a cast ballast keel or internal ballast blocks. Being also a very weak metal and very soft, a lead keel is easily scratched or locally deformed when the boat takes the ground. On the other hand it is easily hammered and filled back into shape again.

The purer varieties of lead 'creep' readily. Over a long period of time an unsupported length of lead – lead pipe for instance – gradually sags. This is not so likely to happen with a solid chunk of lead supported at close intervals by keel bolts, but nevertheless because of the poor creep resistance and because pure lead is so weak, for keels it is better to use a lead alloy. Small quantities of antimony or tin strengthen and harden the metal, and also improve castability. 'Hard lead' is a common name for such a lead alloy. Lead-acid batteries contain about 9% tin; in fact most scrap lead will not be at all pure and will therefore be all the more suitable for keel casting.

Bare lead soon forms a protective surface coating of corrosion product. It is virtually non-corrodible in seawater or fresh water (less than 1 mil per year (25 μm)), especially when primed and antifouled. Lead is another example of the general rule that weaker metals are more corrosion resistant than stronger ones.

Solder is an alloy of lead and tin; the common varieties are 50/50, 40/60 and 80/20. A soldered joint in a water pipe, for example, is perfectly satisfactory for fresh water but sometimes gives trouble due to galvanic corrosion in seawater. It depends on the composition of the solder and on the actual metal of the pipe. If the solder is less noble than the pipe, it will be attacked. The 'area ratio' is far more satisfactory if the solder is *more* noble, so that any attack is spread out over a large area of pipe rather than a small area of solder. The solders high in tin are often less noble than copper, so when a copper pipe is soldered it is better to use 'lead solder', e.g. a 50/50 type. Looking at the galvanic series it will be seen that in seawater solder is actually fairly compatible with copper and brass but not with bronze, Monel or copper-nickel. Always be careful to remove the flux after soldering because accelerated attack can be caused by any residual flux in combination with seawater.

Lead and solder have a low fatigue strength which consequently means that it is positively dangerous to use soldered joints in fuel or gas piping. In a fire, soldered joints might leak fuel or gas, or cause flooding from water piping below the waterline.

Silver brazing is higher in the galvanic series besides being stronger, and consequently makes a better joint particularly with the more noble copper alloys such as the copper-nickels. Silver brazing alloys contain 35–50% silver.

Uranium

It is worth mentioning this exotic metal because it has occasionally been used for yacht keels and may well find more use in the future if its very high price comes down. It is $2\frac{1}{2}$ times more dense than cast iron and about $1\frac{3}{4}$ times as dense as lead, so a keel of uranium can be very slim and compact thus reducing water resistance and improving a yacht's performance. Industrial depleted uranium is a byproduct of the nuclear industry and is used for radiation shielding and balance weights in helicopters. It is slightly stronger than mild steel and is castable (melting point 1130°C). Unprotected, the corrosion rate in seawater is about $1\frac{1}{2}$ inches per year (40 mm) which is a very high rate, but it can be protected by nickel plating. When alloyed with most elements the corrosion rate is much reduced, but even the 8% molybdenum alloy corrodes at $\frac{1}{4}$ inch per year (6 mm). Consequently, as a ballast material it must be encapsulated and protected against abrasion from grounding.

Uranium is very slightly radioactive but can be handled in

complete safety if simple hygiene precautions are taken. These, such as wearing gloves and washing one's hands before eating, apply equally to working with lead.

Titanium

Another exotic metal which will probably have more future impact in the boat world than uranium. Since about 1952 it has been increasingly used in the aircraft industry for jet engine components, airframe parts and guided missiles. It is an extraordinary metal because it is very strong yet very corrosion resistant, and also very light: a unique combination. It is almost as light as aluminium, or put another way, half as dense as steel, and yet even in its weakest form ('pure') it is about as strong as mild steel. Its use in aircraft is also due to its strength at high temperatures.

For marine purposes its total non-corrodibility is most attractive. A tenacious film of oxide is responsible for its corrosion resistance. It only becomes susceptible to corrosion (stress corrosion, in fact) at high temperatures (around 600°F) when exposed to dry salt. Together with its strength and light weight it is finding its way into warship building and it may well seep slowly into boatbuilding.

One obvious application is for keel bolts or fastenings generally. Pure titanium is commercially available in rod, tube or plate form but is very expensive. A titanium keel bolt is likely to be several times the price of a similar sized bolt in nickel-aluminium bronze.

Titanium is very noble in the galvanic scale, slightly above stainless steel, so it is basically incompatible with metals low down in the series like aluminium and steel. But because of its oxide film it causes less galvanic activity than one would expect. For instance in a test of a piece of titanium coupled to a piece of mild steel of the same size, the rate of corrosion of the steel in flowing seawater was only 11 mils per year (0.27 mm) greater than that of bare mild steel by itself, whereas a copper/steel test piece corroded at an additional 69 mils per year (1.75 mm).

What this means is that titanium might be the answer to the old problem of what material to choose for keel bolts in a cast iron keel. The subject of keel bolts is pursued further in Chapter 10 on Problem Areas. Apart from keel bolts, titanium could well find a place on where strength and corrosion resistance are of paramount importance: rigging fittings for instance.

Magnesium Alloys

Even lighter than aluminium, magnesium alloys are used extensively in some industries, but they have very little corrosion resistance in or out of water – even less than steel – and are rarely used in the marine world. They pit rapidly and are also right down at the bottom of the galvanic series.

Types of Corrosion

Chapter 6
Wastage, Pitting and Velocity Effects

Metals can corrode in a variety of distinct and recognizably different ways caused by different corrosives in different situations. Galvanic corrosion is perhaps the most important of these as far as boats are concerned and an appreciation of this topic is essential when it comes to choosing the right metal for the job.

The following list of types of corrosion is by no means complete but embraces the most common:

> General wastage
> Pitting
> Velocity effects including cavitation
> Galvanic
> Electrolytic
> Selective, e.g. dezincification
> Stress corrosion and hydrogen embrittlement
> Corrosion fatigue

The following chapters discuss these one by one.

General Wastage

Table 9 gives typical figures for the overall wastage of unpainted metals immersed in quiet water. These figures assume that accelerated attack due to the other seven factors is *not* taking place.

The nature of the corrosion product often dictates the corrosion rate. If it forms a continuous and impervious layer over the surface and is 'plastic' so that it does not flake off when the metal is strained, and if it is also self-healing when scratched, a corrosion film will completely protect a metal. Stainless steel owes its resistance to such a film; the fact that it also makes a pleasing surface has made this metal very popular. Chromium and aluminium (especially anodised) nickel-base alloys and titanium form similar films.

The maintenance of these particular films depends very much on the presence of oxygen in the water. Reduce the oxygen level and local galvanic action will occur, resulting in deep pits so that while 99% of the metal surface will be virtually uncorroded the pitting may render the complete item unserviceable.

In contrast the less noble metals like copper, brass, lead, steel and zinc corrode faster but in a more uniform manner. The presence of oxygen is detrimental in their case; indeed the corrosion rate of steel and iron is more or less proportional to the oxygen level. In a sealed space steel ceases to rust after a time when all the oxygen is used up. In the same conditions stainless steel is likely to pit catastrophically. There is therefore an anomaly between the capricious noble metals with their highly adherent and protective corrosion films and the gradual 'wasters' at the base end of the galvanic scale that oxidize uniformly.

Table 9 gives figures for metals immersed in ordinary sea and fresh water. In alkaline conditions such as those found when cathodic protection is operating, some of the base metals are badly attacked: aluminium in particular but also zinc and lead. In contrast steel and iron become protected, while the noble metals are unaffected. In acid conditions steel and iron are eaten up, and so are zinc and aluminium. Lead is acid-resistant and is therefore useful for lining battery trays.

In clean air (i.e. away from industry or the sea) virtually all the boatbuilding metals corrode very little with the exception of steel and iron. The rate increases with pollution and with salt sea air, but again it is only steel and iron that give rise to a corrosion problem.

Pitting

Those metals that form thin impervious oxide films, like stainless steel, tend to pit in seawater if the film breaks down for any reason. The small area where the breakdown occurs becomes the anode of a galvanic cell, the large intact film areas being the cathode. Once started the action tends to accelerate rather than stifle itself, so deep pits do occur. The breakdown of the film is usually because of variations in the environment over the surface of the metal: differences in oxygen level, temperature and flow for instance. The potentials on the surface vary, which then initiates the galvanic action. Pitting invariably starts in crevices such as those under washers, in threads or where plates overlap, and under dirt and marine growth sticking to the surface.

Table 10 gives an idea of the probability of pitting of different metals in seawater. Stainless steel is one of the worst offenders while the copper alloys are usually immune. The alloys that tend to pit in *quiet* seawater become virtually immune in flowing aerated seawater and in such an environment they are more useful than copper alloys which, in complete contrast, are happy in quiet seawater but begin to corrode rapidly the faster the flow.

Cathodic protection of the pit-prone alloys either by contact with a large area of base metal (e.g. a stainless bolt in an aluminium plate) or by sacrificial anodes tends to reduce the probability of pitting. (This is discussed in Chapter 1 on Stainless Steel.) Greasing threads with a zinc oxide compound seals against the ingress of water and also the zinc provides some cathodic protection.

Another factor that affects pitting corrosion is alkalinity. The tendency of stainless to pit has been shown to decline as the water over the surface becomes more alkaline. And this is just what happens under cathodic protection. Also, increasing chloride content (saltiness) of the water increases the tendency to pit. In general, fresh waters cause no problems from pitting.

Velocity Effects (Impingement and Cavitation)

As the speed of the water past a metal surface increases beyond 3–6 ft/second 'quiet waters' range (1–2 m/sec), several factors come into play. The pitting of the most noble metals ceases, partly because the water is more likely to be aerated and partly because fouling diminishes. On the other hand the copper alloys begin to lose their protective barrier films and consequently start to corrode rapidly. Steel, aluminium, zinc and lead also corrode rapidly in faster water flows. Tidal or river current flow past a moored boat is most likely to be in the 'quiet water' range (up to $3\frac{1}{2}$ knots).

Problems do occur when a boat is underway; for example, the fast water flow through cooling pipes and pumps, water injection into exhaust elbows, and cavitation. The speed of the water flow varies enormously in these examples. Typical velocities are indicated in Table 11 which also gives a guide as to the corrosion rates of various metals at these velocities. The noble metals like stainless steel and Monel are virtually corrosion-free up to the highest velocities, but most other metals have a definite velocity limit above which the corrosion rate is normally unacceptable. Copper piping, for example, should not be used where the water velocity exceeds about 4ft/sec (1.2 m/sec). Either a more resistant metal should be used or a copper pipe of greater bore. Admiralty brass tubing is more resistant to velocity effects up to about 6 ft/sec (1.8 m/sec), aluminium brass better still at about 8 ft/sec (2.5 m/sec), while 70/30 copper-nickel is good for about 15 ft/sec (4.5 m/sec). The more resistant the metal of the tubing the smaller the internal diameter can be, providing the increased resistance and pressure loss does not become wasteful.

In the design of any water system it is turbulence that creates problems, for instance just downstream of a gate valve seat or a partially opened valve or anywhere where there is a restriction or sudden corner. The local velocities can be very high with consequent local erosion.

The water velocities in pumps are very high and the pump manufacturer has to choose his metals carefully not only from the velocity aspect but also galvanic compatibility.

At very high velocities cavitation is possible and problems do occur on propellers, metal pump impellers, shaft struts and rudders. Cavitation occurs when the local pressure in the water close to a surface falls to almost zero and cavities form. The water literally boils, but without heat. When the bubbles collapse, and if they collapse on a surface, their 'implosion' is so violent that the surface is mechanically attacked and metal is plucked off leaving pits in the surface. Some metals are more resistant to cavitation than others. The basic corrosion resistance of the metal has a bearing on the performance under cavitation; steel for instance is poor. The noble metals relying on a tight oxide film are good. The following list is in order of resistance to cavitation pitting.

88

Titanium Stainless steels Nickel-chromium alloys	The best
Monel Nickel-aluminium-bronze (NAB)	Good
Gunmetal Manganese bronze Copper-nickel	Limited resistance
Cast steel Cast iron Wrought iron Aluminium	Poor

Laboratory work has shown that cavitation resistance increases with surface hardness – or at least the ability of a metal to work-harden. Cathodic protection can successfully stop cavitation, especially if the metal is of a corrodable nature like steel. A powerful overprotection can help in the case of the copper alloys.

Apart from choosing a more cavitation-resistant metal, cavitation erosion can be reduced by better hydrodynamic shaping. On propellers the design of the sections of each blade can be altered to reduce the amount of cavitation. In practice bad cavitation can usually be tracked down to lack of blade area. The propeller thrust per square inch of total blade face area should not exceed a certain amount depending on the top speed of the boat, otherwise cavitation is likely. The value of this pressure in propeller design varies from about 5 psi (0.35 kg/cm^2) at 5 knots to 11 psi (0.77 kg/cm^2) at 30 knots, although the pressure can double before the cavitation covers most of the blade and causes severe erosion and loss of thrust. Making an assumption about the propeller efficiency of average modern yachts and motorboats, one can work out the following propeller blade areas per engine horsepower corresponding to the above permissible pressures:

Knots	Blade area per horsepower	
5	5.6 sq.in.	(36 cm^2)
10	2.7	(17.5)
20	1.25	(8.1)
30	0.63	(4.1)

Again, half these areas per hp would be likely to cause severe cavitation. The blade area on a particular propeller can be simply measured by pressing squared paper onto one blade and counting the squares and then multiplying by the number of blades.

Cavitation causes noise, loss of speed, in extreme cases sudden racing of the engine (on a straight course), and pitting of the blades usually on the after faces towards the tips or near the roots. Fitting a propeller of the same diameter and pitch but with more area, i.e. with wider blades or a greater number of blades, is usually the best cure for boats of up to about 30 knots. Resorting to stainless steel propellers is usually only necessary on very fast craft. Stainless steel is also stronger, which permits a thinner blade section giving a slight improvement in efficiency and speed.

Table 9
General Rates of Corrosion of Bare Metals in Quiet Waters

	Seawater	Fresh water	
Ni-Cr-Mo alloys	0	0	mils per year
Titanium	0	0	
Nickel-chromium alloys	0^1	0	
Stainless steel Type 316	0^1	0	
Stainless steel Type 304	0^1	0	
Copper-nickel alloys (Monel)	0^1	0	
NAB	1–2	0	
Copper-nickels	0.1–0.5	0	
Lead	0.5	0.5	
Tin bronzes	1–2	1	
Silicon bronze	1–2	1	
Manganese bronzes	$1–2^2$	1	
Brasses	$0.5–2^2$	1	
Copper	1–2	1	
Al bronze	$1–2^2$	1	
Austenitic cast iron	2	1	
Steel, iron	5	2	
Aluminium alloys	1–3	0.1	
Zinc	1	0.5	

Multiply mils by 25 for μm/year. The figures are not to be taken very literally and are best regarded as minima, because so many factors can much increase the rate. For instance those marked (1) are liable to pit and those marked (2) are likely to de-alloy. The text describes the factors that cause accelerated corrosion.

Table 10

General Pitting Behaviour of Metals

Zinc Aluminium Steel	Pits tend to be shallow depressions within the general wastage of the whole surface. (Millscale on steel plate causes bad pitting.)
Cast iron Aluminium bronze Brasses Manganese bronze	No problem from pitting but these alloys tend to de-alloy in seawater.
Austenitic cast iron NAB Gunmetal Silicon bronze Copper-nickel Copper inhibited Al brass Lead	Generally no problem from pitting. Pits will be small, if any.
Stainless 400 series Type 304 Nickel Nickel-chromium alloys Type 316 Monel Alloy 825 Alloy 20	Entire corrosion is due to pitting. This list is roughly in the order of tendency to pit, the 400 series being worst with severe pitting. Pitting of the last three is usually no problem and Type 316 can successfully be used with cathodic or galvanic protection. Cathodic protection is likely to be more successful the lower the metal on the list.
Alloy C Alloy 625 Ni-Cr-Mo alloys Titanium	Virtually no attack from pitting nor any other corrosion.

TYPES OF CORROSION

Table 11
Maximum Likely Corrosion Rates at Various Velocities (mils/year)

	Seawater 0–3 (0–1)	Velocity: 6–12 (2–4)	ft/sec 20–50 (6–15)	(m/sec) 120–140 (35–45)
Zinc	3			
Aluminium alloy	pits			
Steel, iron	5	20–30		300
Austenitic cast iron	3		10	30 +
Aluminium bronze	low		resistant	
Brass	dezincs	5 +		
Manganese bronze	dezincs		resistant	
Copper	3	5 +		
Aluminium brass	2	5 +		20
Silicon bronze	low			
Gunmetal	low		10	40 +
90/10 Copper-nickel	1	1	5 +	30
70/30 Copper-nickel	1	1	1	7
Lead	low			
NAB	2		10	30 +
Stainless steel 304, 316	pits	1	1	1
Monel	may pit	1	1	1
Ni-Cr-high Mo alloys	nil	nil	nil	nil
Titanium	nil	nil	nil	nil

Quiet water	0–4 or 6 ft/sec
Pipe design velocity	4–12 ft/sec
Pump impellers and propellers	30–80 ft/sec

Multiply units by 25 for μm/year.
Gaps denote a lack of test data.

Chapter 7
Galvanic Corrosion

In the year 1763 a group of gentlemen reported to their Lordships of the Admiralty on the success and the failure of an experiment whereby HMS *Alarm* had been copper sheathed under water and sent to tropical waters. Success, because the copper had indeed prevented fouling and attack by teredo worm. Failure, because some of the fastenings were of iron and the rudder pintles and various other items at the stern were also iron.

'We were greatly surprised to perceive the Effect the Copper had had upon the Iron when the two metals touch'd; but it was most remarkable at the Rother iron and in the fastenings of the false Keel, upon the former, the Pintles and Necks of the Braces were as corroded and Eat – particularly the two lower Ones that they could not have continued of sufficient strength to do their Office many Months longer, and with respect to the false Keel it was entirely off.'

Since that time many other people have 'been greatly surprised' by the rapidity and destructiveness of galvanic corrosion. But even today the reaction of boat builders can be much less enlightened than those gentlemen two centuries ago. 'Bad bit of metal' or 'Erosion by sand' are often modern boat builders' comments. And yet in their report those far-off gentlemen realized what was wrong, because they had observed that when brown paper had separated the two metals far less corrosion of the iron had taken place. They suggested that the false keel be held on with copper and that all parts unavoidably made of iron should be covered with sheet lead.

Copper sheathing became common practice, but the simple and easily understood theory behind galvanic corrosion is yet to be appreciated by many boat builders and owners.

TYPES OF CORROSION

Even in 1915 a very expensive mistake was made when a large yacht was built of Monel with the exception of the stern keel, stern-post and rudder frame which were made of iron. Both Monel and iron rivets were used. After a few weeks many of the iron rivets failed and leaked and upon close inspection serious corrosion was found of the steel parts exposed to the water. Whoever backed the venture decided to give up and the vessel was scrapped. Yet around that time several other large yachts were made of copper and nickel alloys and proved successful. The answer to the whole business lies principally in the galvanic series, discussed below.

Place two different metals in seawater, connect them with a wire, and an electric current will flow from one to another (9). The voltage created can be enough to light a torch bulb, depending on the metals chosen and the area exposed to the water. A galvanic cell is set up – a battery in fact – and the unfortunate part of the phenomenon is that as current is generated one of the metals is very

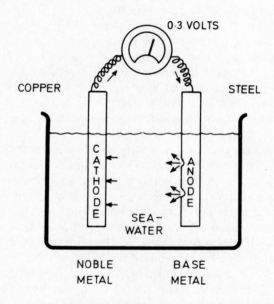

(9) A galvanic cell. The cathode metal is protected, the anode metal eaten away. The seawater around the cathode becomes alkaline. Galvanic cells can be set up on underwater fittings made of different metals, or on deck.

rapidly corroded. The other metal's corrosion rate is slowed or stopped, however. (This also happens in the common household battery: the zinc casing gets eaten away until the battery is flat.)

The liquid surrounding the two metals – the electrolyte – has to be able to conduct electricity. Seawater is a very good conductor, fresh water is much less conductive, and pure water is a very poor conductor. Obviously the degree of conductivity of the liquid directly affects the rate of corrosion.

Galvanic cells are set up when two different metals are immersed in a conducting liquid and also they are electrically connected either by touching or by a metallic path. Examples are easy to bring to mind: a bronze seacock in a steel hull, a brass screw in an aluminium fairlead. In the latter case although the item is not under water, it will be wetted and drops of water will lie between the screw's head and the aluminium, sufficient to set up a vigorous reaction (10).

The Galvanic Series

Each metal immersed in a particular electrolyte has a certain electrical potential, i.e. capacity to generate electrical currents.

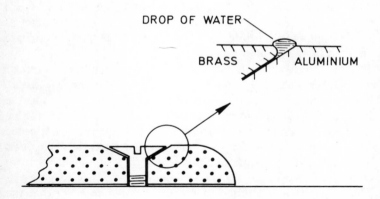

(10) Dissimilar metals on deck will corrode galvanically in a very local fashion. In this instance the drop of water causes a powerful cell to be set up, corroding the aluminium very rapidly even if the water is rain rather than salt.

95

TYPES OF CORROSION

Measure the voltage of a piece of copper and it will be different to that of say steel in the same liquid. In another electrolyte the voltages may be different. This electrical 'rating' leads to the formation of a table listing the metals in the order of their electrical potential. It is called a galvanic series (11) and the one for seawater is commonly published. It is a very useful table that really is a vital tool for anyone choosing metals for marine use. It is useful to the boat owner who is completing a fibreglass hull, embellishing his boat with extra fittings, or trying to cure a corrosion problem.

Published galvanic series often do not quite agree with one another, even those dealing solely with seawater as the electrolyte. The exact composition of the metal or alloy has an effect on the place it occupies in the series, the exact nature of the seawater (polluted or clean) also has a bearing, and so too does the nature of the surface of the metal (abraded or corroded). The temperature and velocity of the seawater electrolyte can also have an effect.

The metals high up in the series (11) are said to be more 'noble' than those lower down, which are said to be 'base'. This is a convenient way of expressing their relative positions when talking of two different metals. Other terms are less clear, for instance 'cathodic' and 'anodic' meaning 'noble' and 'base' respectively. Some tables are shown upside down, but commonly the noble metals like silver, bronze and copper are listed above the base metals such as zinc and steel. After a while this natural 'social strata' becomes easy to remember, especially as the noble metals corrode but little while the base ones generally corrode more readily.

In order to establish a galvanic series the electric potential of each metal is measured relative to a constant reference electrode, the most common being the 'saturated calomel half-cell' and the 'silver/silver chloride half-cell'. If a metal is more noble than these references it is said to have a positive potential, and if it is less noble (which is more often the case) a negative potential. The two reference electrodes mentioned are only 0.02 volts different from each other.

The one misleading thing about the galvanic series is that the voltage potential differences between two particular metals does not give a direct and realistic indication of the corrosion to be expected. Double the voltage difference does not necessarily mean

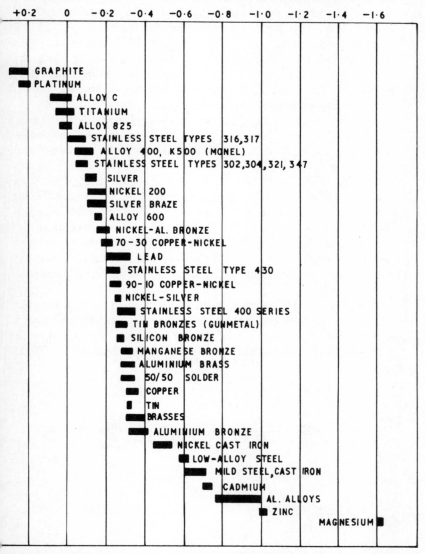

VOLTS RELATIVE TO A SATURATED CALOMEL HALF-CELL

+0·2   0   −0·2   −0·4   −0·6   −0·8   −1·0   −1·2   −1·4   −1·6

- GRAPHITE
- PLATINUM
- ALLOY C
- TITANIUM
- ALLOY 825
- STAINLESS STEEL TYPES 316,317
- ALLOY 400, K500 (MONEL)
- STAINLESS STEEL TYPES 302,304,321,347
- SILVER
- NICKEL 200
- SILVER BRAZE
- ALLOY 600
- NICKEL-AL. BRONZE
- 70−30 COPPER-NICKEL
- LEAD
- STAINLESS STEEL TYPE 430
- 90−10 COPPER-NICKEL
- NICKEL-SILVER
- STAINLESS STEEL 400 SERIES
- TIN BRONZES (GUNMETAL)
- SILICON BRONZE
- MANGANESE BRONZE
- ALUMINIUM BRASS
- 50/50 SOLDER
- COPPER
- TIN
- BRASSES
- ALUMINIUM BRONZE
- NICKEL CAST IRON
- LOW-ALLOY STEEL
- MILD STEEL, CAST IRON
- CADMIUM
- AL. ALLOYS
- ZINC
- MAGNESIUM

(11) The galvanic series. This one is a modern and generally accepted series, but in practice the actual potentials vary with many factors such as temperature, salinity, movement in the electrolyte, etc. Stainless steels and Alloy 600 may become active in crevices or under barnacles, the potential then being near −0.5 volts. Pitting will then take place.

double the corrosion: all it indicates is the voltage. The corrosion rate is dictated by the *current* that that voltage creates, and the current flow is influenced strongly by several factors:

(a) If an ammeter is put in the circuit in (9) it will be seen that quite quickly after 'switching on' and connecting the electrodes, the current drops off to some steady and much lower value. This effect is called polarization and some combinations of metals show a greater degree of polarization than others.

(b) Often those metals that have a tough oxide skin polarize rapidly and therefore cause much less corrosion to their less noble mate than one would expect from the galvanic series. Stainless steel is an example.

(c) The respective areas of metal exposed to the electrolyte has a very significant effect. If a large area of noble metal acts on a small area of base metal the attack is concentrated on this small area and the corrosion is very rapid (12). When the situation is reversed, as for example a bronze (noble) seacock in a mild steel (base) hull, the small area is attacking a large area and the corrosion is spread out and becomes less noticeable. This 'area ratio effect' as it is called is a vital factor.

In a galvanic cell the base metal is attacked and in contrast the noble metal is protected. In fact, in some cases it will become plated with the base metal – a form of electroplating. Of course as soon as the whole area of noble metal is covered the galvanic cell will fizzle

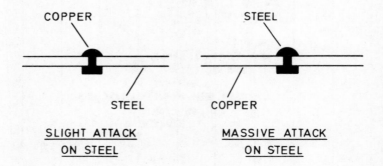

(12) Area ratio effect. On the right a large area of copper is attacking a small area of steel and the steel bolt will corrode away in a very short time. On the left the copper's attack is spread out over a large area.

98

out. The action stifles itself, providing the coating is not stripped away by the cleaning action of a water flow, for instance, because bare noble metal will then be exposed again and the corrosion of the base metal will recommence. The reaction will also be stifled if the base metal forms a coat of corrosion product (rust on steel, for example), but if the rust is removed the attack will start again.

In fresh water the galvanic series is much the same in terms of the order of different metals, but the important difference in terms of galvanic corrosion is that the action is much more local than in seawater. Seawater, being such a good conductor of electricity, will 'throw' the effect over quite a large area: the current 'density' (amps per square foot, for example) diminishes quite slowly with distance from the noble metal. In fresh water the current falls off rapidly with distance. Whereas a brass screw in a steel plate in seawater will cause general corrosion of the steel over a large radius, in clean fresh river water the effect will be far more local because of the poor conductivity of the water.

On deck or aloft the effect again is very localized; corrosive action takes place in tiny pools of water or under damp salt particles. The area ratio here is likely to be 1:1 and no help can be expected from this factor. A brass screw in a galavanized bollard only represents a small area in relation to the bollard, but the galvanic activity will be very local around the periphery of the head of the screw.

A few general rules to avoid galvanic corrosion can be stated:

(a) Make all parts of the item of the same metal or alloy.

(b) If this is not possible (which is usually the case), make the more important or the smaller item (e.g. the fastening) the more noble *or* electrically insulate the different metals.

(c) Arrange the area ratio the right way round so that the metal liable to be corroded presents a large area in order to spread the attack. Also make sure that the base metal is of ample thickness to allow for corrosion.

(d) In the same vein, keep to a minimum the exposed area of the more noble metal. This can often be done simply by painting the noble metal, and insulating it with a gasket or flexible compound where it is in contact with other metals.

TYPES OF CORROSION

Insulation

Electrically insulating is not as difficult as it sounds. In practice impermeable plastic, neoprene or Tufnol gaskets, washers and sleeves are fitted between the items, or between the fastenings and the item (13, 14). Lack of electrical continuity can be checked simply with a battery and bulb, or better a sensitive voltmeter. In practice, insulation usually works very well.

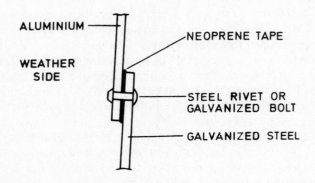

(13) A joint suitable for an aluminium deckhouse on a steel hull. The joint should be painted over and should be arranged not to trap water. The bolts could be of stainless steel.

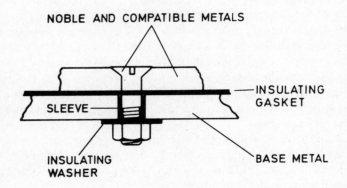

(14) The principle of insulation, shown in this case where two different metals are bolted together. Tufnol is often used as the insulator.

In larger craft aluminium deckhouses are often welded to a steel deck by means of a bi-metallic strip. This strip comprises steel and aluminium layers explosively bonded together. The steel part is welded to the steel deck and the aluminium part welded to the aluminium deckhouse. Provided the explosively bonded interface does not get too hot (max 350°C) the joint is very strong, reliable and avoids galvanic problems. DETACOUPLE and KELOCOUPLE are two proprietory names of such joining strips approved by most classification societies.

Fastenings

Table 12 gives a guide as to what metal to use as a fastening in fittings of various materials. It is generally best to make the fastening of the same material, or one which is more noble, so that it is galvanically protected. But too great a separation in the galvanic series leads to excessive corrosion of the base metal around the fastener and the bolt hole may become enlarged. The copper alloys are very destructive to aluminium; but Monel and particularly stainless steel, although they are even higher in the series, show little attack. Note that aluminium fastenings can only be used in aluminium; despite its oxide film this metal is readily attacked even if the area ratio is favourable. Zinc coatings are also readily stripped off by galvanic action.

The copper alloys (brasses, bronzes, etc) are also 'lively', especially in flowing seawater, and it pays to follow the rules when two of these alloys are in contact even though the voltage difference in the galvanic series may be slight. For example, a silicon bronze bolt in a 70/30 copper-nickel plate in seawater will suffer even though these two alloys are close together; whereas, reversed, the fastener is protected and the attack on the base metal is minimal. Careful inspection of the galvanic series will reveal slight differences of potential within the copper alloys and the simple rules for preventing galvanic action should be observed.

Stainless steel fastenings are very useful because they are compatible with a wide range of metals. Even stainless steel bolts set into aluminium are acceptable, except that the aluminium thread will corrode and seize, so it is better to use a stainless steel threaded insert.

It will be noticed that graphite is very noble, and if graphite grease is used on a thread or in a propeller shaft bearing severe local attack of the metal will result. A molybdenum disulphide type of grease is safer.

Nail-Sickness

The electrical path between the noble and the base metals shown (9) does not have to be as obvious as an electrical wire or two metals touching. Surface damp on fibreglass, or wet wood, will conduct electricity to some extent, thus completing the circuit between, for example, iron keel and an adjacent bronze seacock. The corrosion rate depends largely on the distance between the two and also on the moisture content of the wood or the dampness of the inner skin of fibreglass. Certainly it is bad practice to position dissimilar metal items very close together (say less than 6 in. or 150 mm) and it is obviously wise to keep them as far apart as possible, especially if they are both close to the bottom of a wet bilge.

This galvanic effect can loosen copper clenches or nails in a wooden boat and is commonly called 'nail-sickness' (15). What

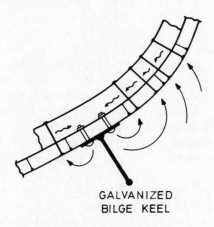

GALVANIZED
BILGE KEEL

(15) Nail-sickness. The damp timber acts as a conductor of the galvanic current. The resulting alkaline condition around the copper clenches in time decays the timber and makes the fastenings loose.

happens is that the wood adjacent to the copper becomes alkaline after a time, which is detrimental to most woods and causes them to decay. The fastenings thus become loose despite the fact that they are galvanically protected. Nail-sickness is often caused by an iron keel, but it takes many years for a boat to be so afflicted. Other factors which will much reduce the effect are: (a) keeping the timber at a low moisture content, helped by lifting out during the winter; (b) a sound paint scheme, partly to keep the timber dry and partly to cover the heads of the clenches; (c) a sound paint scheme on the iron keel; (d) keeping the bilges dry and the protruding bolts inside the boat well painted.

A sound and well maintained wooden hull will have dry timbers; and dry wood is a poor conductor of electricity. It is usually old or neglected boats that are found to be suffering from nail-sickness. Timbers most resistant to alkali attack include teak, pitch pine, Honduras mahogany and most softwoods (on the other hand, softwoods are more likely to decay from fungi, i.e. to rot). African mahogany has a low resistance.

With fibreglass hulls the same phenomenon has not yet been a problem though strong alkalinity, surrounding a zinc anode for example, has been thought to have caused local blistering.

Antifoulings

Copper-based antifoulings can cause very extensive galvanic corrosion of galvanized bilge keels, aluminium hulls and outdrives, and indeed any item made of a base metal. A barrier coat of paint can be used to create insulation between the hull and fittings and the antifouling, but nowadays copper-free antifoulings are readily available and are suitable for all base metals.

Conclusion

Appreciation of the meaning of the galvanic series is the vital key to understanding most of the corrosion problems on board boats. The rest is easy!

Table 12

Galvanic Compatibility Underwater or On Deck for Salt Water Craft

Fitting	Fastener							
	Galv.	Al. alloy	Cadmium plated	Steel	Brass,[1] Bronze	Monel	Type 304	Type 316
Galvanized	N	?[3]	C[3]	C	x	x	C[4]	C[4]
Al alloy	C[8]	N	C[8]	C[4]	x	C[4]	C[4]	C[4]
Cadmium plated	x	x	N	C	x	C[4]	C[4]	C[4]
Steel, iron	x	x	?[2]	N	C[4]	C[4]	C	C
Brass, bronze	x	x	x	x	N[1]	C	C	C
90/10 Copper-nickel	x	x	x	x	x	C	C	C
Lead	x	x	x	x	C[6]	C	C	C
70/30 Copper-nickel	x	x	x	x	x	C	C	C
Monel	x	x	x	x	x[7]	N	?[5]	?[5]
Type 304	x	x	x	x	x[7]	C	N	?[5]
Type 316	x	x	x	x	x[7]	?[5]	?[5]	N

N = Neutral

x = Not compatible, i.e. severe corrosion of the fastener will take place.

C = Compatible.

[1] Including aluminium bronze, silicon bronze, all the brasses, copper, manganese bronze, gunmetal and 50/50 solder. Refer to galvanic series for compatibility.

[2] The plating will soon be stripped off.

[3] Better to use galvanized.

[4] May lead to some local corrosion of fitting around fastener.

[5] Higher chance of pitting under head.

[6] Lead is another relatively inert metal as far as galvanic action is concerned.

[7] Better to use the same metal for the fastener as for the fitting.

[8] Not immersed.

Note: Brass and manganese bronze tend to dezincify underwater. Stainless steels tend to pit underwater or in wet wood unless galvanically protected *all over* by the fitting metal.

Chapter 8
Electrolytic, Selective and Stress Corrosion and Corrosion Fatigue

Confusion often exists between electrolytic and galvanic corrosion. The difference is quite simple: whereas galvanic corrosion is caused by an electric current generated by two different metals in a conducting medium such as seawater (a 'seawater battery'), electrolytic corrosion is caused by a current from an *external* source, often the boat's battery or a shore supply. This means that even two *similar* metals can form the cathode and anode of a cell, the anode being corroded (16). The current that causes electrolytic action is called

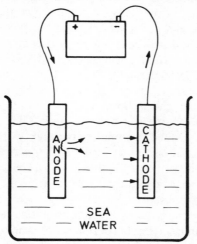

(16) Electrolytic corrosion is different from galvanic corrosion in that the current is supplied by an external source such as the boat's battery or a shore supply. The metals may be similar or dissimilar. The driving current might well overcome any galvanic current and force a noble metal normally aloof from galvanic corrosion to corrode.

'stray current' and usually emanates from a poorly installed electrical circuit or a bad earthing arrangement, on power tools or a radio for instance, or a current leak due to damp conditions. The underwater metal item which grounds the leakage will be corroded and in the case of brass or bronze will be bright in appearance, as if brand new.

The rate of electrolytic corrosion can be quite frightening because the stray current may be anything from a trickle (because of damp, for instance) to a deluge from a short circuit; there is no inherent limitation as with galvanic corrosion.

Preventing electrolytic corrosion is a matter of good electrical installation. The wiring system should be 'insulated return' (two wires) rather than 'earth return' (one wire, as in a car where the body of the car forms the return circuit). A metal hull must never be used as the earth return.

A battery master switch should be fitted on the battery positive terminal and turned off when the boat is idle.

Earthing (grounding) is required for safety if voltages are high, as when an onboard 240 volt generator is fitted or a shore supply arranged. Earthing in this sense is not to be confused with 'earth return'. Earth return carries current; earthing or grounding involves a third wire which does not carry current, just like a house system. Earthing can also be necessary to reduce radio interference. This is achieved by electrically linking the screening around the radio to all the other items of equipment and hence to a common earth. This linking is called 'bonding'.

When a petrol engine is fitted the deck filler plate, tank and engine should be earthed to avoid the possibility of sparks occuring when the bowser makes contact with the filler *plate*.

On less sophisticated boats – those without electronics or shore supply – it is unnecessary to earth. Better to make sure the underwater metallic fittings are electrically isolated. This in practice means measures such as fitting an insulating coupling on the propeller shaft (many flexible couplings are insulating) and using a short length of plastic or neoprene pipe in the piping to seacocks (good practice to reduce vibration and metal fatigue, in any case). In this way there will be no metallic path, and unless damp creates an electrical path there should be no chance of electrolytic corrosion. A battery switch will help to eliminate the last possibility, and of course such a switch – turned off – is a wise precaution against finding a flat battery after a week or so.

Bonding to Earth

Without delving too far into the realms of electrical installation, the earth (or ground) should consist of a sacrificial plate on the underside of the hull well away from the propellers, etc. Heavy gauge insulated earth wire or a non-insulated metal bonding tape should run fore and aft above the bilge water level and off the hull itself, connecting all the large metal items together with short branches off the main tape (17). The object is to avoid electrical disparity between the various metallic parts such as engine, generator, radio cabinets, screening, fuel tanks, battery trays, etc. The bonding tape is connected to the earth plate. The earth should not be an existing underwater fitting.

Since the object of the electrical bonding is to achieve a low-resistance link, the connections must be well made: if not soldered or brazed, bolted. Avoid bolting dissimilar metals together because in sea air galvanic corrosion will quickly lead to a high impedance across the joint.

On a metal hull a separate bonding system is unnecessary providing electrical continuity is maintained between the hull, engine and other items required to be earthed. This can be checked with a tester made from a battery and bulb.

As with cathodic protection, although the principles of electrolytic corrosion are simple, effecting a cure is often difficult and it is wise to call in a specialist.

Selective Corrosion

Sometimes called de-alloying, the most common form is the *dezincification* of brasses and manganese bronze as discussed in Chapter 2 on Copper Alloys. Dezincification involves the dissolving out of the zinc alloy of brass leaving a red crumbly mass which has little strength. Brass screws in wet wood, at least in seawater, dezincify very readily. Indeed any brass fastener underwater

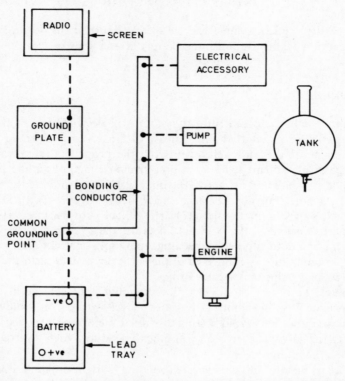

(17) Electrically sophisticated boats need a bonding system. With non-metallic hulls the bonding conductor (uninsulated) should be no smaller than No. 6 AWG wire, held above bilge water and run fore and aft. Jumpers leading from this cable should be No. 8 AWG soldered to the main wire. Note that this system must not carry current: it must not form part of any electrical circuit. A metal hull can form its own bonding conductor.

is liable. So too is a manganese bronze propeller shaft or propeller since manganese bronze is *not* a bronze but a brass. Brasses with more than 15% zinc are very liable to dezincification unless 'inhibited'; brasses with less than 15% are usually immune.

GRAPHITIZATION occurs in cast iron; in this case the iron corrodes out leaving a graphite mass which is also soft and yields to a penknife. Nickel cast irons with 2–3% of nickel are less susceptible, while austenitic cast irons are immune.

DE-ALUMINIFICATION is a horrible word for the de-alloying of aluminium bronze. Advice on the reliability of aluminium bronze is rather contradictory, but if it has 4% or more nickel (i.e. is nickel-aluminium-bronze) the problem is averted.

WELD DECAY occurs in austenitic stainless steels and is a form of selective corrosion. This topic and the prevention of the problem are dealt with in Chapter 1 on Stainless Steel.

Cathodic protection will often stop dezincification. A manganese bronze propeller on a steel boat suffers very little corrosion whereas on a wooden or fibreglass boat dezincification can ruin it within a few years. Cathodic protection also inhibits iron, and would probably inhibit aluminium bronze but information on that point is lacking.

Stress Corrosion Cracking

Stress corrosion occurs in some metals when subjected to a steady tensile stress, rather than compression, while wetted with a particular corrosive. Each metal has its own *bête-noir*.

The stress level at which stress corrosion cracking can occur is well below the normal breaking strain of the metal. It suddenly fails by cracking; there is no warning since the crack is often invisible to the naked eye and can propagate rapidly once started. Quite how stress corrosion cracking occurs is still not clearly known, but pitting due to corrosion or some other stress raiser like a notch or a sharp corner clearly creates the starting point for a crack to develop. Metal that has cracked due to this type of corrosion usually shows little actual corrosion and the break is mostly clean. Of course as the crack propagates inwards the remaining intact metal becomes more highly stressed until eventually it breaks through sheer stress.

Table 13 sums up the metals that are prone to stress corrosion. Generally it is the high-strength metals that suffer, while such benign materials as mild steel, copper, gunmetal, silicon bronze, etc are immune under boating conditions.

Since only the lower strength aluminium alloys are used in boat building there is generally no problem from stress corrosion with the exception of N6. This has 5% magnesium and can crack when used in rivet form, as mentioned in Chapter 3 on Aluminium Alloys. The rivetting process stresses the metal, and if salt water is added and also a hot climate the heads can fall off. But the other marine grades including the casting alloys of aluminium are immune even when highly stressed.

High-tensile steels that enter the strength region where cracking can occur are only likely to be used in boats as a bolt material. Clearly this is a case where it is better to use a lower strength steel bolt of greater diameter. This is a very valid point for keel bolts in an iron keel: never use a high-tensile steel.

Brass can crack even during manufacture if exposed to small traces of ammonia or mercury, and this is called 'season cracking'. Stress corrosion cracking is far less of a problem than dezincification when brass or manganese bronze are used underwater, while above water the evidence (or lack of it) suggests that these alloys are trouble free.

Stainless steel is susceptible to stress corrosion cracking in chloride conditions, but only at higher temperatures (usually given as over 150°F) and when the metal contains residual stresses due to manufacture or load. A great deal of research has gone into the failures of stainless steel in the chemical and power industries, where the combination of chlorides and high temperatures in particular have caused trouble. Although seawater contains chlorides, and stresses are usually present, stainless steel fittings at normal temperatures rarely crack, that is unless weld decay is responsible. Weld decay can be overcome simply by using the correct grade of stainless (e.g. 304L and 316L) and is explained more fully in Chapter 1 on Stainless Steel.

Barring weld decay, the other possibility is if stainless steel is used for a water injected exhaust pipe, for example, where the temperature is high. Even here the metal should not be under load and therefore not so susceptible to cracks. Indeed the pipe should ideally be stress-relieved after manufacture to make sure that locked-in stresses are reduced.

Salt deposits on stressed parts of the standing rigging can be the cause of cracking, especially in a hot climate. Imagining the worst situation – a poorly designed rigging screw for instance, with an abrupt 'necking', causing a large stress concentration, add a stainless steel other than Type 316 and a rough surface finish. Tension the screw and sail in windy conditions with heavy spray flying and a hot sun. Then leave the boat on her mooring for a few weeks during which time there is no rain to wash the heavy salt crystals off, but every night imagine that dew falls and the salt crystals melt to form a highly concentrated chloride film. These are the conditions which lead to a broken mast.

Good design, a rainy temperate climate, the use of Type 316 stainless and the problem disappears – providing that if welding has been a part of the manufacturing process the proper precautions have been taken. Annealing to relieve locked-up stresses caused by forming and shearing during manufacturing processes is also an effective way to reduce the probability of cracking.

In general the chance of stress corrosion cracking can be much reduced by a protective coating like galvanizing on steel, or paint or lanolin, or by cathodic protection, though the latter will only work on underwater items.

'HYDROGEN EMBRITTLEMENT' can be included under the heading of stress corrosion cracking since it causes cracking in a stressed metal, but in this case hydrogen is the corrosive medium. Some metals are prone to absorb hydrogen when this gas is present on the surface, subsequently causing cracking. The only metals with this tendency, in the context of boatbuilding, are high strength steels and some stainless steels. High strength steels become susceptible where the yield strength exceeds about 90 tons per square inch (1400 N/mm^2). This fact becomes pertinent in two particular instances. First, where a high tensile steel bolt is immersed in seawater and is cathodically protected by being either zinc coated or 'protected' by a sacrificial anode. Hydrogen may be evolved on the surface which then may be absorbed leading to cracking. Second, galvanized high tensile steel chain can crack during the galvanizing process though the requirements of high tensile material, a high internal stress due to manufacture and thick sections are necessary before the problem rears its head. Yacht-sized chains are rarely troubled, partly because of the relatively thin section and partly because steels above the susceptible limit of strength are not used. Subsequent failures in seawater are not a continual problem.

Non-austenitic hardenable stainless steels with yield strengths of more than 90 tons per square inch are susceptible to hydrogen embrittlement. Types 316 and 304 are immune. Yet again the policy of only buying 304 or 316 pays off; ensure that the grade is austenitic by taking a magnet into the yacht chandler's and checking that the stainless is non-magnetic.

Corrosion Fatigue

This type of corrosion again leads to sudden and unexpected cracking. While stress corrosion is the result of a combination of steady tensile stress and a corrosive medium, corrosion fatigue comes from the combination of *alternating* tensile and compressive stresses and a corrosive medium. While the difference in terminology may appear to be slight, the important point is that while only a few boat metals are susceptible to stress corrosion practically *all* metals can suffer corrosion fatigue.

First of all, consider fatigue by itself, without a corrosive medium. A piece of metal like a paper clip can be fractured easily by bending it to and fro a few times. In doing this the metal is stressed right up to its yield point at every stroke; the stress on the surface of the clip will alternate between high compression and high tension. Now if a lesser stress is applied at each bending, the clip will take much longer to break. The lower the stress the greater the number of cycles before fracture: if the stress is low enough the pin will never break. This stress is called the fatigue limit, the safe working stress for an infinite life.

The 'time to fracture' for various stress levels can be plotted out to form what are called S-N curves (18), meaning Stress – Number of cycles. The curve, which is usually obtained with the test piece in air, is different for different metals.

In seawater or any corrosive medium including fresh water, rain water and damp salty air, metals do not achieve the same fatigue resistance as in air. Curve B in (18) represents what happens when corrosion is present. Not only does the metal crack sooner for any particular stress but there is no fatigue limit; even at a very low stress level almost every metal fails eventually. In effect this means that every cycle of bending or alternating stress causes damage: the

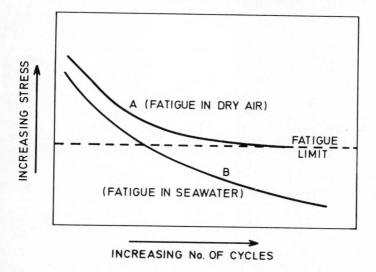

(18) Fatigue curves (S-N curves) of metal in air and in seawater. In clean air there is usually a level of stress below which a metal can take any number of stress reversals without cracking: this is called the fatigue limit. But in seawater there is no unlimited area; some time or other the metal will break even at a very low stress. At high stress levels many metals need only a few reversals to fracture, as when bending a paperclip back and forth.

metal's life is irreparably shortened.

The graph (19) shows curves for the fatigue corrosion of a few boatbuilding metals, while Table 14 shows the fatigue strength of metals at 100 million cycles. This number of cycles may seem a great many, but take for instance a standing wire stay humming in the wind. The frequency of a typical boat stay in a strong wind is somewhere in the order of 50 Hz (cycles) every second. So in an hour that is 180,000 cycles and in a day 4.3 million. Hence 100 million is reached in only 23 days of strong winds. The magnitude of the stress is obviously a deciding factor as to how long the stay or its end fittings will last.

Again, if engine or propeller vibration is the cause of the alternating stresses then even at 1,000 rpm it takes only 1,600 running hours to reach 100 million cycles. There is no magic in the figure of 100 million but it is often taken as a yardstick by engineers. As can be seen in Table 14, the fatigue strength at this

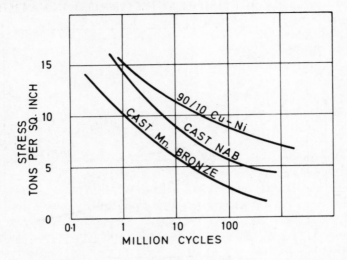

(19) Corrosion fatigue curves (see also (17)) for three copper alloys, determined by tests on samples in seawater. Cast manganese bronze for instance has to go through ten million cycles of stress reversals with a maximum stress in each cycle of 6 tons per square inch before a fatigue crack appears. 90/10 copper-nickel is much stronger in the sense that it can take a higher stress for the same life.

point is a small fraction of the tensile strength of the metals.

Mild steel is the least resistant metal in terms of its strength at 100 million cycles. Manganese bronze is far better, while stainless steel (Types 316 and 304) has seven times the fatigue strength of mild steel. In terms of life this has an even larger effect assuming that the same stress level is used in the different materials.

A corrosion resistant metal is likely to have better corrosion fatigue properties. Another factor is if the item is cathodically protected either by a sacrificial anode or by being in contact with a less noble metal. For instance zinc-coated steel shows a far greater corrosion fatigue strength than mild steel. A case in point are tangs and shroud plates: these should be galvanized if made of steel. Similarly it is a happy coincidence that small steel shackles are invariably galvanized to stop rusting. If steel is plated with a *more noble* metal like chromium, the fatigue strength is *reduced*.

Failure from corrosion fatigue can never be guaranteed because there is no fatigue limit, but in practice there are four ways of ensuring a long, long life: (a) use a corrosion resistant metal; (b) keep the stresses low by overdesigning – be generous when deciding on the sizes of wire rope, shackles, etc; (c) if steel is used choose galvanized; (d) most important, avoid stress concentrations.

Taking this last point, consider a badly designed rigging screw (20). The stress raisers are shown. A weld is particularly bad if it has inclusions and if it has only a small bead. Sharp corners and screw threads are also stress raisers. Smooth 'streamlined' designs are good; so too is a smooth surface.

A fatigue fracture usually propagates from a small surface pit or a sharp corner and leaves successive 'beach marks' on the broken edges. The final snapping leaves a distinct crystalline area. It is very difficult to detect cracks before failure because they are so small. A penetrating dye and a magnifying glass is a simple though not infallible method but hardly the activity of a busy boat owner. Overdesign (robust sizing) is his best protection together with corrosion resistant metals and good detail design.

Stainless steel is so commonly used for boat items that a few specific points on this metal are worthy of mention.

Types 304 and 316 have a fatigue limit in clean air of about one-half of their ultimate tensile strength (i.e. for one single pull). In seawater at 100 million cylces this is halved again, but even so this represents a stress of about 6 or 7 tons per square inch (100 N/mm^2) which is far higher than any designer would dare to

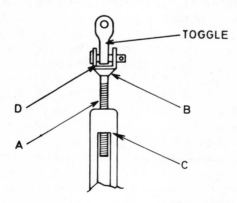

(20) A toggle at *each* end of a rigging screw reduces the bending stresses at A and also the chances of corrosion fatigue. Welded joints as at B are poor practice; so are sharp corners as at C and D.

use as a working stress for boat fittings where a large factor of safety on yield is required. So provided bad stress raisers are not present and that welds (if any) are generous in size, well done, ground off and smoothed, and a good factor of safety is used, stainless fittings of Types 304 and 316 give little trouble from corrosion fatigue.

Fatigue-Conducive Conditions

Wind in the rigging has been mentioned as a source of fluctuations of stress. Eddies of air shed off the mast in a wind make it vibrate; this can be felt quite plainly. Taut rigging also hums. Broken strands are a sure sign that the wire rope has come to the end of its life and should be replaced quickly. Galvanized wire rope should also be suspected as soon as rusting appears. Boiled linseed oil applied annually is the traditional method of extending the life of galvanized wire.

Rolling is a source of alternating stresses in such items as the rigging, the rudder and keel bolts. A small yacht typically completes a roll in 3 seconds which represents 30,000 cycles per day, and a million cycles in 33 days. Yachts on exposed moorings could well suffer from rolling fatigue, especially if the shrouds are left slack so they snap taut at every roll.

Engine vibration can travel throughout a boat and can cause fatigue cracks in the mounting brackets for instance, quite apart from all the moving parts of the engine itself (although these one hopes have all been properly designed and tested with fatigue in mind). A copper fuel line or water pipe that is too rigidly connected to the engine (especially if the engine is flexibly mounted) is liable to leak at the joint and eventually to fatigue. The simple answer is to fit a short length of flexible hose close to the joint on the engine.

Any part of a boat that vibrates badly is prone to fatigue. The propeller also gives rise to vibrations and fluctuating stresses; in steel boats the hull plating above the propeller has been known to crack within a short time. Mild steel has a very low corrosion fatigue strength; the cure is to stiffen the panels of plating with flat bars or insert a thicker plate.

Of course propellers, propeller shafts and shaft brackets, and rudders are subject to fatigue, but due to the fact that corrosion resistant materials are usually used and that the design stresses are deliberately kept low, fractures are few and far between.

Steel and aluminium hulls even when built of the thinnest practical plate are immensely strong and the stresses imposed by the sea are very, very small. Consequently fatigue in the hull structure is generally no problem, except in the case mentioned above.

WATERJETS While waterjet propulsion is still not common in leisure craft it has become the norm in fast ferries which are invariably built in aluminium alloy (5083 and 6082). It is interesting to observe that three corrosion phenomena have caused considerable difficulties to designers builders and operators alike. The first is fatigue (or corrosion fatigue) in the structure surrounding the waterjet. This has occurred because large forces are created by the water jets besides the vibratory forces from the impellor blades at blade passing frequency.

The situation is made worse by the presence of seawater both outside and in the bilges, and most importantly by the inevitably intricate structural design in these areas. This means that the structure is far from smooth and there are many stiffeners passing through each other causing stress concentrations. Of course the whole structure is welded, compounding the fatigue problem.

Aluminium alloy has a nominal UTS of 15 tons/sq.in. (5083). Its fatigue strength in air is about 7–8 tons/sq.in. at a reasonable number of cycles (10^7) tested on a smooth unwelded sample. Put this in seawater and the corrosion fatigue drops to about 2.5 tons/sq.in. Weld it and this drops by one half again. Add stress raising details and the picture is not one of great performance!

The second problem is that of erosion at high water velocities. Where the boundary layer is thin or where the local velocity is raised, the aluminium surface can be rapidly eroded away. This happens in the inlet duct to the tunnel.

The third problem is galvanic. The impellors and shafting and sometimes the jet casing are made of a high grade of stainless. Housed inside an aluminium tunnel and mounted on an aluminium transom this is a recipe for corrosion, but it can be controlled by passive or active cathodic protection. However, deep recesses within the jet are not easy to protect, and it is here that deep and rapid galvanic corrosion can take place.

Table 13 Susceptibility to Stress Corrosion Cracking

Susceptible metals	Environment
Very high strength steels (with yield strength of over 90 tons per square inch (1,400 N/mm²)	Seawater, fresh water, on deck
High strength aluminium alloys (with yield strength of over 25 tons sq. in. (400 N/mm²) Wrought aluminium alloys with more than 3% magnesium	Seawater, fresh water, on deck
Stainless steels: Type 304 Type 316	In hot seawater or salt crust at above 150°F. Steam and hot caustic soda.
Carbon steel (caustic cracking)	Hot caustic alkali
Brass with more than 15% zinc, and manganese bronze	Seawater and ammonia (polluted seawater)
Aluminium brass Aluminium bronze	Ammonia + steam

Not susceptible in normal boating conditions in or out of the water:

Copper	Aluminium alloys
Titanium	Lead
Stainless steel Types 316 and 304 (may pit underwater)	Copper-nickels
Silicon bronze	Gunmetal
Aluminium bronze	Aluminium brass
Mild steel and cast iron	
Nickel-based alloys, e.g. Monel and Ni-C alloys	
Nickel-aluminium-bronze	
Brass and manganese bronze *on deck*	

Table 14 Corrosion Fatigue Strength of Various Metals at 100 Million Cycles, in Seawater

Material	Ultimate tensile strength: tons/sq in (Kg/mm²)	Corrosion fatigue strength: tons/sq in (Kg/mm²)
Mild steel	27 (42)	0.9 (1.4)
Cast manganese bronze	32 (51)	3.6 (5.6)
Cast nickel-aluminium-bronze	39 (61)	5.6 (8.8)
Type 316 stainless steel	38 (60)	6.1 (14)
Type 304 stainless	35 (56)	6.7 (10.6)
Monel K-500	80 (124)	10.6 (18.3)
Hastelloy Alloy C	48 (76)	14.3 (22.5)
Inconel Alloy 625	58 (91)	18 (28.2)

Control and Prevention

Chapter 9
Cathodic Protection: the Corollary of Galvanic Corrosion

Corrosion can be reduced or stopped completely by cathodic protection. The area to be protected is made the cathode (the relatively noble end) of an electric cell; that is to say, instead of current leaving that area and thereby causing corrosion, the current is forcibly reversed thus stopping the corrosion (21). Cathodic protection can be applied wherever there are galvanic cells causing

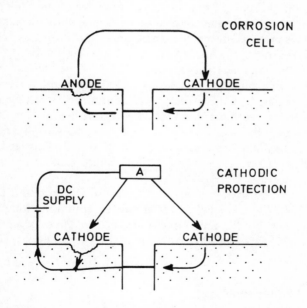

(21) The principle of cathodic protection: A may be either a sacrificial anode (replacing the DC supply) or an impressed current anode.

corrosion; for instance two different metals in electrical contact with each other and in water, or alternatively the tiny corrosion cells on the surface of an impure metal such as steel. Indeed the most common use of cathodic protection is on steel ships.

There are two types of cathodic protection in use, first the sacrificial anode type and second by means of impressed current. As its name suggests, sacrificial anode protection involves electrically coupling a base metal to the more noble item to be protected which then becomes the cathode; a zinc block on a steel hull for instance. The zinc corrodes steadily while the steel is protected, and when the zinc block is nearly exhausted it must be replaced. This is by far the most common method in boats and the rounded lozenge-shaped zinc blocks are a familiar sight bolted to the underwater hull, usually in the region of the stern.

The impressed current system has revolutionized ship hull maintenance in the last decade. Previously sacrificial anodes were commonly fitted to ships since Davy in 1824 suggested the concept of cathodic protection, but the recent growth in ship size and the much greater effectiveness of electronic control units for impressed current systems has meant that most new ships have this superior method of protection. Instead of using a sacrificial anode to create a counter current, electricity is pumped into the water from an inert non-corrodible anode. Unlike a sacrificial system, the current flow, can be regulated to the precise level necessary for complete protection. Bare steel thus protected ceases to rust in seawater. But the current requirement is too high to contemplate abolishing paint in favour of cathodic protection on a steel boat hull. This technique, however, is the practice in some ships' ballast tanks and on some oil rigs.

At present not many boats are fitted with an impressed current system. Large luxury steel yachts are the exception, although some outboard and outdrive manufacturers such as Mercury and OMC do offer a kit to protect their aluminium drive legs and propellers.

Sacrificial Anodes

The sacrificial anode is simply bolted to the hull and in the case of a non-metallic hull wired up to the item to be protected (22). It is

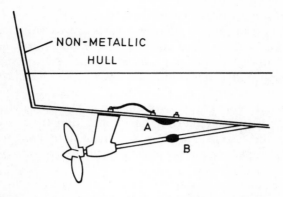

NON-METALLIC
HULL

A

B

(22) A simple example of sacrificial protection. Anode A is wired to the shaft bracket while B is bolted directly onto the shaft. Cathodic protection like this is only necessary if the materials of the shaft, bracket or propeller are of unreliable alloys like manganese bronze, brass or stainless steel, or if dissimilar metals are electrically connected. If gunmetal, silicon bronze, Monel or NAB are used cathodic protection becomes unnecessary.

very important to obtain a resistance-free electrical circuit and consequently heavy gauge wire should be used and the connections should be well made and kept on the inside of the hull and clear of bilge water. The current flowing through the circuit is quite small, but any resistance reduces the voltage difference between the anode and the cathode thus directly reducing the protection. An internal wire is far preferable to an external metal strip which inevitably will suffer galvanic corrosion itself at one of the junctions and thus create a resistance to electrical current.

On a metallic hull, electrical continuity is ensured simply by bolting the anode direct to the plating with welded-on studs.

There are three types of anode: zinc, magnesium and aluminium. These base metals will give protection to all other metals higher in the galvanic series, so virtually all the common metals used in boats can be protected. The protection so achieved may not be complete, or it may be excessive, depending on the voltage difference generated and the current flowing into the protected area per square metre. And that depends on the exposed area of the anode and its efficiency. For each particular boat the required number and size of anodes can be calculated using factors determined from previous installations. The aim is to give the required degree of

123

protection with a reasonable life from the anodes.

The accompanying drawings and notes are based on literature from M. G. Duff for small craft (see Some Addresses). Note that wood and fibreglass hulls are treated separately from steel hulls. On wood and GRP hulls mild steel items must have a separate anode to the one protecting the more noble items (brass propeller, stainless shaft, etc). The two systems must be electrically separate; there must be no internal electrical connection from say a steel rudder to the engine. Anode size is related to the area to be protected; propeller diameter gives a rough idea of the size of this area, hence the table of propeller diameters.

On steel boats stud-fixed anodes are recommended rather than the welded-on variety since they are easier to replace. Small craft only require a small number of anodes; those less than about 25 ft. in length require only two, one on each side.

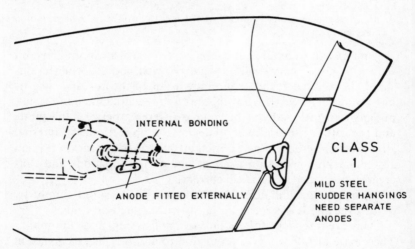

INTERNAL BONDING

CLASS 1

MILD STEEL RUDDER HANGINGS NEED SEPARATE ANODES

ANODE FITTED EXTERNALLY

(23) Zinc anode location and sizes for wooden or fibreglass hulled boats in seawater (based on M. G. Duff recommendations)

CLASS 1 VESSELS comprise single-screw sailing yachts, motor cruisers, fishing vessels, launches etc with only a very small or negligible length of propeller shaft exposed to seawater; they are fitted with mild steel rudders, *or* wood or GRP rudders with mild steel hangings.

As a general rule for Class 1 vessels, one anode will be required for propeller and propeller shaft protection, plus two separate anodes for rudder protection. The main anode should be located on the hull bottom below the turn of the bilge, its fore-and-aft position roughly equidistant between the engine gearbox and the in-board end of the sterntube. The additional anodes are fitted directly to the rudder.

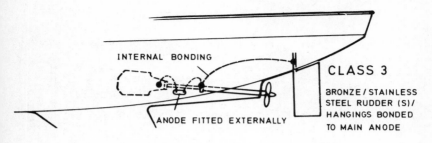

INTERNAL BONDING

ANODE FITTED EXTERNALLY

CLASS 3

BRONZE / STAINLESS
STEEL RUDDER (S)/
HANGINGS BONDED
TO MAIN ANODE

CLASS 3 VESSELS are the same as Class 1 but with bronze or stainless steel rudders, *or* wood or GRP rudders with bronze or stainless steel hangings.

As a general rule, one anode can provide protection for the propeller, propeller shaft and rudder, and should be located as for Class 1 vessels.

CLASS 2

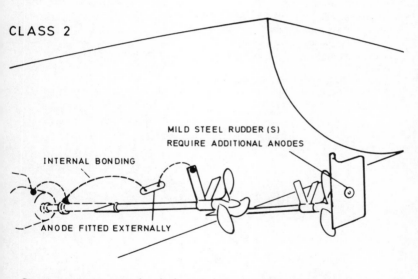

MILD STEEL RUDDER (S)
REQUIRE ADDITIONAL ANODES

INTERNAL BONDING

ANODE FITTED EXTERNALLY

CLASS 2 VESSELS comprise single or twin screw sailing yachts, motor cruisers, fishing vessels, launches etc with a long length of propeller shaft exposed to seawater; they are fitted with mild steel rudder(s) *or* wood or GRP rudder(s) with mild steel hangings.

Generally, one anode is required for *each* propeller to give it and the shaft protection, and also two separate anodes for each rudder. Locate main anode(s) in way of exposed shaft(s). The main anode(s) can also provide protection for the bronze brackets carrying the propeller shaft. The additional anodes are fitted directly to the rudders.

125

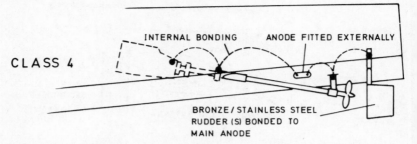

CLASS 4

INTERNAL BONDING   ANODE FITTED EXTERNALLY

BRONZE/STAINLESS STEEL
RUDDER (S) BONDED TO
MAIN ANODE

CLASS 4 VESSELS are the same as Class 2 but fitted with bronze or stainless steel rudder(s), *or* wood or GRP rudder(s) with bronze or stainless steel hangings.

Generally, one anode can provide protection for one propeller, propeller shaft, shaft bracket and rudder. Locate anodes as for Class 2 vessels.

Note: In all classes of vessels the positioning of anodes is not critical. The main points to remember are:
—Can the anodes 'see' the parts to be protected?
—Are the fixing studs above the bilges?
—Does the anode location ensure the minimum run of bonding cable to the parts to be protected?
—Is there reasonable internal access to the studs?

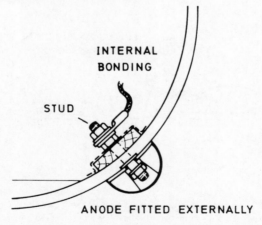

INTERNAL
BONDING

STUD

ANODE FITTED EXTERNALLY

ANODE INSTALLATION ON HULLS   Decide on a suitable position for the anode for propeller protection (see above). Fit a wood block to the inside of the hull (glassing it in if GRP). Bore holes to take the fixing studs. Recess the outer surface of the hull to allow the stud collars to lie flush when tightened in place. On the outside of the hull fit the backing sheet, then the anode. Attach bonding cables to the inner length of the studs.

126

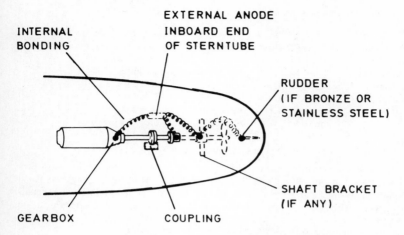

INTERNAL
BONDING

EXTERNAL ANODE
INBOARD END
OF STERNTUBE

RUDDER
(IF BRONZE OR
STAINLESS STEEL)

SHAFT BRACKET
(IF ANY)

GEARBOX   COUPLING

BONDING From the anode fixing studs inside the hull bonding cable is taken to the engine gearbox and the inboard end of the propeller shaft sterntube; also to other bronze or stainless steel fittings where applicable, e.g. rudder(s) on Class 3 or 4 vessels. *Anodes should not be bonded to mild steel fittings*, e.g. mild steel rudders or rudder hangings on Class 1 or 3 vessels.

Care must be taken to ensure good clean and tight connections for all anode installation and bonding. Where any form of insulated coupling is fitted in the propeller shaft line it is necessary to bridge it with a bonding strip.

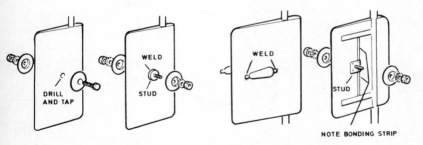

DRILL
AND TAP

WELD

STUD

WELD

STUD

NOTE BONDING STRIP

ANODE INSTALLATION FOR RUDDERS, RUDDER HANGINGS AND MILD STEEL SKEGS In the case of mild steel rudders or skegs, two anodes can be fitted back-to-back by bolting to the rudder or skeg; or to studs welded to the rudder or skeg. Strip anodes can also be bolted to steel rudders. In the case of wood or GRP rudders with mild steel hangings, all anodes can be fitted onto stud plates which are screwed to the rudder and galavanized strip taken from the stud plates to the steelwork for bonding.

CONTROL AND PREVENTION

Class of vessel	*First decide the class of your vessel. Read across to the propeller diameter, then down that column to the bottom of the table.*		
Class 1	up to 14 in.	up to 29 in.	30–36 in.
Class 2	up to 11 in.	up to 21 in.	22–30 in.
Class 3	up to 12 in.	up to 26 in.	27–33 in.
Class 4	up to 10 in.	up to 19 in.	20–26 in.
	one 0.9 kg (sailing aux. yachts only)	one 2.2 kg	one 4 kg

MILD STEEL RUDDERS, SKEGS AND BILGE KEELS Anodes for protection of these areas are generally fitted directly to the steelwork. Mild steel fittings painted to normal seasonal standards with suitable paints (*NB*: red lead primers and metallic copper antifoulings are *not* suitable) can be protected according to their surface area:

> up to 10 sq. ft. of steelwork: two 1.35 kg (strip anodes)
> up to 30 sq. ft. of steelwork: two 0.9 kg
> up to 70 sq. ft. of steelwork: two 2.2 kg

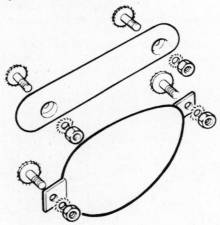

(24) Zinc anode locations and sizes for steel hulled boats in seawater (based on M. G. Duff recommendations)

WETTED SURFACE AREA CALCULATIONS Using the main dimensions of the vessel in feet or metres (waterline length, breadth and mean loaded draft) calculate area by the formula LWL x (Breadth + Draft). The resulting area applies to trawlers, tugs, ferries, motor cruisers, launches and full-bodied sailing craft. Multiply the calculated area by 0.75 for medium displacement craft, by 0.5 for light displacement craft.

Spoiling the ship for a ha'penny of tar.

Plastic coatings do not last long in a marine environment; the slightest nick in the coating and corrosion of the metal underneath soon peels the coating back. This prop had only done 30 hours.

Notice how the proper stainless fittings are pristine while the painted mild steel ones are bleeding rust like mad.

How different metals perform on deck. The galvanised stem head roller is fine but rough, the cast and anodised aluminium cleat and hawse pipe are little pitted and dulled while the stainless pulpit is still shiny. Galvanised chain lasts some 10 years.

For solid integrity you can't beat bronze or gunmetal fittings.

Even in sheltered positions, chromium plated finishes really don't remain long in showroom condition.

This winch would look better now if it had never been chromium plated in the first place.

Bare mild steel fuel tanks are best avoided except as a short term solution. Apart from the obvious corrosion problems inside the tank (from water in fuel and condensation) and outside, there is the safety risk of rust particles entering the fuel system and causing engine failure.

Even inside a cabin, damp salt air takes its toll. The steel base plate of the light plus its chromium plated bezel have suffered by being near an opening window. Mirrors too suffer around the edges.

Successful galvanic protection. After a year's immersion the anode is partially eaten away, the steel rudder is rust free and the prop appears to be protected as well (evidenced by the barnacles).

Dust to dust! All materials are eventually turned back to the constituents from which they came. Maintenance and care is the thing that slows the process.

When seawater is allowed into a thrust bearing or gearbox in quantities
more than a few per cent of the oil capacity, the results are disasterous.

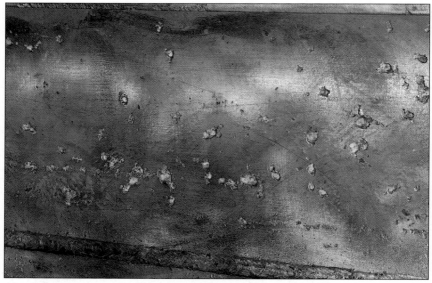

Aluminium water tanks if unprotected can suffer internal corrosion like this
one here. The pitting has occured in 6082 plate. 5083 is more resistant; the
alternative is to paint the inside.

Jets and outdrives often look a corroded mess when the boat is taken out of the water. Strong cathodic protection encourages calcium deposits and barnacles. Bolts or hose fittings, which are of sub-standard stainless, bleed rust. Joints exude corrosion products and it's usually the least noble metals that take the brunt of any corrosion.

While this damaged propeller above and broken shaft below were the result of going aground the fracture inevitably occurred at the weakest point – the end of the keyway. The shape of the keyway in the shaft is important in order to avoid premature fatigue cracking. (Mcgruer & Co Ltd)

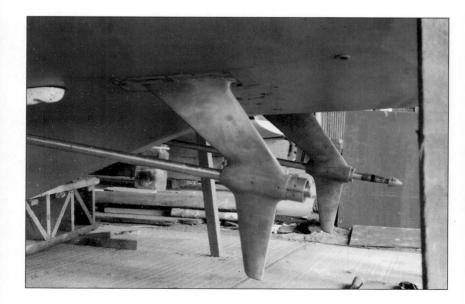

CATHODIC PROTECTION

ANODE SELECTION FOR ONE YEAR'S FULL HULL PROTECTION

Wetted surface area	Stud-fixed anodes	Additional anodes recommended for twin-screw craft	
Up to 300 sq.ft. (28m²)	two 4 kg	two 1 kg	per rudder
301–600 sq.ft. (28.1–56 m².)	four 4 kg	two 1 kg	,, ,,
601–900 sq.ft. (56.1–84 m²)	six 4 kg .	two 1 kg	,, ,,
901–1100 sq.ft. (84.1–102 m²)	four 6.5 kg	two 2.2 kg	,, ,,
1101–1600 sq.ft. (102.1–148 m²)	six 6.5 kg	two 2.2 kg	,, ,,

ANODE SELECTION FOR TWO YEARS' FULL HULL PROTECTION

Wetted surface area	Stud-fixed anodes	Additional anodes recommended for twin-screw craft	
Up to 300 sq.ft. (28 m²)	four 4 kg	two 2.2 kg	per rudder
301–500 sq.ft. (28.1–46 m²)	six 4 kg	two 2.2 kg	,, ,,
501–700 sq.ft. (46.1–65 m²)	eight 4 kg	two 2.2 kg	,, ,,
701–900 sq.ft. (65.1–84 m²)	four 12 kg	two 4.5 kg	,, ,,
901–1350 sq.ft. (84.1–125 m²)	six 12 kg	two 4.5 kg	,, ,,
1351–1800 sq.ft. (125.1–167 m²)	eight 12 kg	two 4.5 kg	,, ,,

STUD-FIXING ANODES Mark off positions of anodes as shown below or as directed. Mark positions of studs on shell plating. Scale to bare metal in way of these positions in preparation for welding studs to hull. Make a continuous fillet weld around the stud plates. Paint hull area before fitting anode to studs. Fit serrated washer and nut and tighten up hard. *No paint should be allowed to fall on the surface of the anode itself at any time.* Anodes should be renewed when about 80% consumed.

POSITIONING The drawings below indicate anode positions in relation to the water-line length of the vessel. Positions can be adjusted slightly to suit the vessel and to avoid locations in way of echo-sounding transducers or impeller logs.

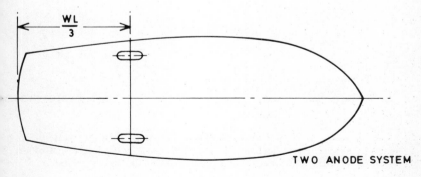

TWO ANODE SYSTEM

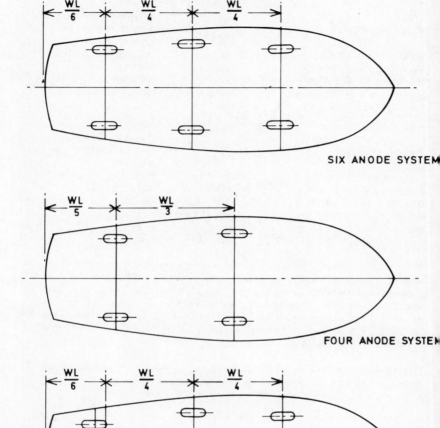

SIX ANODE SYSTEM

FOUR ANODE SYSTEM

EIGHT ANODE SYSTEM

EXAMPLE: twin-screw motor cruiser 35 x 11½ x 3¼ ft. Area = 35 x (11½ + 3¼) = 516 sq.ft. Anode selection for say one year, stud-fixed. Quantity (from table above) for wetted area 301–600 sq.ft. range: four 4 kg zinc anodes plus two 1 kg per rudder.

130

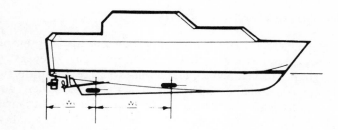

To achieve the correct degree of protection it is always best to ask a specialist in cathodic protection for an estimate of the number, size and position of the anodes, rather than make a haphazard guess. Sacrificial anodes can be bought over the yacht chandler's counter, but to merely bolt them on without advice is a waste of money and can cause consequential troubles. Such specialists advertise in the yachting magazines; they can give individual advice and supply the relevant anodes. Installation is a relatively simple DIY job.

It is not uncommon to see an anode bolted to a wooden or fibreglass hull without any wiring to couple it up; or sometimes the anode is painted over! In both situations it is absolutely useless. The proof that an anode is working is that it gradually corrodes away over a period of several seasons. It must never be painted.

Zinc anodes are most often used rather than magnesium or aluminium. The zinc needs to be of a high purity or have only small amounts of certain elements which are not detrimental to its performance. Iron as an impurity is very harmful because it leads to the formation of a heavy adherent film over the anode which of course reduces the current flow. So the best zinc for use as an anode is a special material and certainly not commercial zinc. US Military Specification 18001H is a common one.

Magnesium gives a higher-driving voltage, which may be useful, but it has a low efficiency in terms of the electricity it can generate per kilogram weight.

Aluminium also has a higher driving voltage and modern special alloys developed specifically for anode material can be used for particular applications. Again, the specialists in cathodic protection will suggest the best material for any particular situation.

Fibreglass and Wooden Hulls

Ideally the metallic items below water should be made of one of the more seawater resistant alloys like silicon bronze, copper, gunmetal, copper-nickel, nickel-aluminium-bronze or one of the super-materials like titanium and the nickel-base alloys. If any one of these is electrically isolated and not connected, for instance via metal piping, to the engine (thus bringing the possibility of corrosion from stray currents) there will be no need for cathodic protection. Isolated from any possible galvanic action, they will merely corrode at a very slow rate.

But all too often dissimilar metals are in contact or the metals themselves are not seawater resistant: steel for instance, or stainless steel, manganese bronze or brass. In any of these situations cathodic protection can be used to suppress the electrical currents generated and hence reduce or stop corrosion.

A steel rudder is protected by an anode bolted directly to it. So is a cast iron keel, but oddly enough anodes bolted here are rarely seen despite the saving in maintenance they would bring. In the case of a manganese bronze or brass propeller or shaft dezincification can be reduced or eliminated by an anode bolted to the hull, but electrical contact has to be maintained to the rotating shaft. Sliprings on the shaft are one possibility, but far from ideal because they will need frequent cleaning. There may be electrical continuity from propeller to engine in which case the engine can be grounded to the anode, but often a rubber flexible shaft coupling is employed which acts as an insulator. The propeller shaft bearings may be rubber or bronze: obviously rubber will act as an insulator and continuity across a grease film in a bronze bearing is not reliable enough. The way out of this situation is to fit a collar type of anode around the shaft itself or to the propeller boss.

The same argument applies if the shaft or propeller are of stainless steel. Stainless tends to pit underwater in crevices and under barnacles; on shafts, pitting often occurs in way of a rubber bearing or in the thread or keyway. Cathodic protection may reduce the possibility of pitting. It is certainly worth fitting a zinc anode, but the cathodic protection given may not reliably extend to shielded areas – which are just those where pitting may occur.

Seacocks should *not* be made of brass or manganese bronze but of silicon bronze or gunmetal, for example. So often, though, some internal parts of the gate valve type of seacocks are made of a brass or manganese bronze and hence tend to dezincify. It is doubtful if cathodic protection would 'reach' into the seacock, especially when it was closed.

With ferrocement hulls it is essential that galvanic cells involving the steel reinforcement are avoided. All underwater fittings except steel for galvanized ones should be electrically isolated from the reinforcement. This is especially the case with any fittings of copper alloys, e.g. seacocks and sterngear. It is another reason for coating the hull with a very waterproof paint scheme such as three coats of epoxide composition.

Outboards and Outdrives

Invariably outboards and outdrives are made of aluminium and often have built-in sacrificial zinc anodes in the form of small blocks or rings around the propeller fairing. While marine grade aluminium alloy is very corrosion resistant in isolation, it is so low in the galvanic series that all the other common boat metals will attack it galvanically if there is an electrical path. The sacrificial anodes incorporated do guard against this to some extent but it is very wise to ensure that any 'heavy metal' items (brass, bronze, etc) are physically several feet away and have no direct electrical connection to the outdrive. For example an engine cooling seacock of bronze could be coupled via copper piping to the engine which in turn is coupled to the out-drive. Flexible rubber hose and flexible couplings cut this electrical contact but there may be a link through a control cable, and the best check to establish whether there is a link is with a sensitive voltmeter. A copper fastened wooden boat can give trouble to an aluminium outdrive, the electrical path in this case being through damp timber. Also in time the hull fastening may become loose through 'nail-sickness' described above. The only palliative is to paint the stern area around the out-drive with a thick impenetrable paint, epoxide for instance.

It is essential to electrically isolate an outdrive or an outboard when mounted on a steel boat but not of course when on an aluminium hull.

On the same theme, never use a copper-based antifouling on an outdrive powered boat or an aluminium hull. Nor, for that matter, on *any* hull if sacrificial anodes are fitted.

The drag of sacrificial anodes will theoretically slow a boat down although the reduction is immeasurable on sailing yachts and displacement craft. Even on a planing boat the streamlined lozenges cause an unnoticeable loss of speed.

If a boat lies at moorings for most of her life a system whereby anodes are hung down in the water might be attractive, especially with a steel hull. The anodes must be hung well clear of the hull to give an even spread of current (and to stop the zinc blocks banging on the sides) and they must be electrically coupled to the hull (hung on wire rope). A bare piece of steel can also be hung in the water and electrically connected to the hull as a control. It should remain unrusted if the cathodic protection is working. Again, a consultant's advice should be sought because there are possible pitfalls involved in cathodic protection, as explained later.

In America in particular close-spaced marina berths are sometimes fitted up with impressed current systems designed to protect groups of boats, particularly aluminium ones. Correctly installed and adjusted for the type and number of hulls being protected, the system is fine. But conditions can change drastically if boats move away or if others of different hull material move in. It is possible to get a situation where one's own boat is feeding current to an adjacent one via a small underwater area closest to the other boat, which will cause rapid corrosion.

Impressed Current Systems

Unlike the sacrificial anode type of cathodic protection, which creates a counter current by a deliberately made galvanic cell, the impressed current system uses electricity from a battery or transformer fed from a shore supply. The principle of making the metal item to be protected a cathode remains the same, but the current flow per square metre can be adjusted to give the optimum protection. The sacrificial anode system is 'fixed' in this sense; its current output is unalterable once installed.

Impressed current systems are mostly used on steel hulls; most new ships have the system. For steel boats the practical problem of an impressed current system is often the electrical supply. If the boat's berth has a shore supply all well and good, but it is impractical to use the boat's batteries because of the amount of current required day and night. Assuming the current density was 50 mA/m^2, a 10 metre boat would consume about 1½ amps, i.e. about 250 amp hours a week. Very large batteries and a charging system would be needed. An impressed current system using the battery can only in practice be used to protect small items such as an outdrive. The anode from which current flows to protect the steelwork consists of an inert electrode mounted on the hull and lasts for ten years or more. The current is supplied to the anode from a DC supply and controlled either automatically or manually to give the correct potential on the hull.

To completely protect a steel hull the potential must be lowered from about –0.65 volts without cathodic protection to about –0.85 volts, these voltages being relative to a silver/silver chloride electrode immersed in the water nearby. To achieve this, the current flowing into the steel hull will vary according to the type and thickness of paint and its age. New epoxide paint will be a very good insulator and the current flow need only be 10 to 20 mA/m^2 of surface area. A completely bare steel hull would need about 100 mA/m^2. Other variables include the salinity of the water and whether the boat is moving or not. Consequently one can see that a sacrificial anode system having a fixed potential might when new give too much protection and after a few years give too little. An impressed current system can compensate all the time. A reference electrode is fitted in the hull to measure the potential difference achieved when the cathodic protection is switched on.

The anode to which the regulated current is supplied is made of silicon iron or titanium, for example, coated with platinum or a lead-silver alloy. The paint on the steel hull immediately adjacent to the anode usually has to be protected from the powerful current by an insulating shield of epoxy or fibreglass. Or it may be an integral part of the anode. Because seawater is such a good electrolyte, anodes, including sacrificial ones, can 'throw' their current over considerable distances. Of course the current density drops off with distance from the electrode, but two anodes can easily cover a small steel boat hull. (Conversely, of course, galvanic corrosion can

'throw' its activity from say a bronze seacock amidships to a galvanized rudder pintle aft.)

Snags with Cathodic Protection

As with any galvanic cell the area of water around the cathode
(the protected item) becomes alkaline: the greater the protective
potential the greater the alkalinity. Traditional types of paint – oil
or lead-based ones for example – are softened and blistered by
alkali. Hydrogen bubbles may also be formed under the paint surface depending on the porosity of the paint, thus lifting it off. The
chances of either of these things happening is greater the higher the
potential applied, so zinc sacrificial anodes are 'safest' while
magnesium anodes or an impressed current system are worst. If a
steel hull is overprotected or has a porous oil-based paint scheme
the paint may 'saponify' as it is called, but the bare steel thus exposed will be protected against rusting. The answer is to make sure
that overprotection is not being applied and then to use a more
resistant paint. An aluminium-bitumen or chlorinated rubber paint
is resistant, or even better are vinyl or coal tar epoxy or epoxide.

The alkaline conditions around protected aluminium can cause
its corrosion rather than its protection, so an aluminium hull is
better cathodically protected by zinc anodes rather than
magnesium. On the other hand, since marine grade aluminium in
isolation is corrosion resistant there is little point in cathodically
protecting an aluminium hull unless there are also more noble
metals used underwater (a bronze propeller for instance). The
correct protection for aluminium in seawater is –0.985 volts relative
to a silver/silver chloride electrode.

The hydrogen given off may cause 'hydrogen embrittlement' of
high strength steels including some stainless steels (400 series). This
has happened to bolts on outdrives fitted with an impressed current
system.

Turning now to wooden boats, the production of alkalinity
around protected metals can cause decay of the adjacent timber.
This effect is the same as the nail-sickness mentioned earlier and is
accentuated by overprotection, a porous paint scheme and time
(five years plus). The timber becomes a soft and fibrous mass and
one of the indications that the action is taking place is the presence

of white crystal deposits on the inside of the hull around the protected item. Quite apart from cathodic protection, electrolytic action from strong currents may also cause this type of degradation.

In a sense one chooses between installing low quality, low cost underwater fittings and then protecting them by cathodic protection with the risk of timber degradation, or alternatively installing fittings of a corrosion resistant metal or alloy and ensuring their electrical isolation. The latter method must surely be the best policy in the long run.

Finally in this catalogue of gloom there is the need to be aware of what may happen when your metal hull is moored adjacent to another metallic mass, for instance steel piling, another metal hull alongside or a steel marina pontoon. Trouble is avoided if there is no electrical link; plastic fenders and synthetic rope are good enough insulators. But suppose there was a link through an aluminium gangway, for instance, or a wire rope. A cathodic protection system will then suddenly find it has a great deal more area

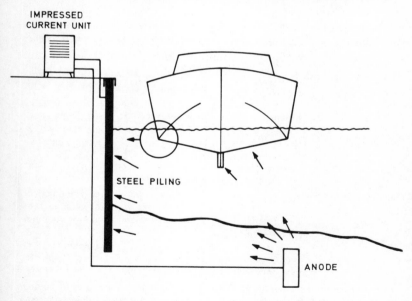

(25) Another possible source of trouble occurs if a metal boat is moored near a jetty whose steel piling is cathodically protected. The current will try to take a short-cut through the hull and exit in a small area closest to the jetty, causing rapid corrosion.

137

to protect (in say a steel hull/steel pontoon combination). The protection from zinc anodes will be shared and the protection on one's own boat will drop; while an impressed current system will try to compensate – probably unsuccessfully – causing very high potentials local to the anode, and blistering of the paint on the hull.

Mention should also be made of simple galvanic cells created by an aluminium hull moored to a steel one and in electrical contact, or a steel hull to a copper-sheathed wooden one again in electrical contact. In the first case the aluminium hull will suffer, in the second the steel. The rate of corrosion will depend very much on the resistance of the electrical contact and on the porosity of the paint film, and whether there are any areas of bare metal. Certainly an owner of a metal boat should bear this sort of thing in mind when mooring her in her permanent berth.

Table 15

Metals Which can be Prevented From Corroding in Seawater by Cathodic Protection

Small area of:	Type of failure underwater	Cathodic protection by a much larger area of:	Or a sacrificial anode of:
Monel	Pitting[2]	Bronze down to steel[1]	Steel, zinc. Aluminium or magnesium.
Stainless steel	Pitting	Bronze down to steel[1]	
Mn bronze	Dezincification	Steel	
Al brass	Dezincification[2]	Steel	
Brass	Dezincification	Steel	
Al bronze	De-aluminification[2]	Steel	
Steel and iron	Rust	Zinc or aluminium	Zinc, aluminium or magnesium
Cadmium	Fast general corrosion	Zinc or aluminium	Zinc or magnesium
Zinc	Fast general corrosion	—	Magnesium

The metals listed here can be prevented from corroding in seawater by cathodic protection: either by using a larger area of less noble metal already there (e.g. a steel hull), or by adopting sacrificial anodes or an impressed current system.

[1] Referring to the galvanic series.
[2] Relatively low risk.

Chapter 10
Underwater Problem Areas

Keels and Keel Bolts

External ballast keels for sailing yachts are commonly made of cast iron. It is suitably dense and relatively cheap. On a long-keeled boat an iron keel makes a tremendously strong backbone and a robust 'shoe' for taking the ground. Cast iron brings two problems: rust, and the material of which to make the keel bolts.

The problem of rust with an iron keel is just the same as the rust problem on a steel hull and the solutions are the same too. Paint is the first answer. Conventional steel primers and top coats under the antifouling give a short life and such a scheme will probably need laborious cleaning and re-coating every two or three seasons. Higher performance paints such as epoxy applied on a shot-blasted surface will give a much longer life, except on the underside of the keel where inevitably the coating will be scraped off.

Galvanizing is impractical (unless a galvanizing bath can be found that is big enough), but aluminium or zinc spraying is an effective second best that surprisingly is not often used but would give many rust-free years at quite a moderate increase in cost. The coating must then be painted with an appropriate paint scheme for an aluminium or zinc surface, otherwise it will disappear in no time.

Another seldom used practice is a sacrificial anode bolted to each side of the keel. This is a classic example of the use of anodes; the extra water drag involved is too small to be noticed. Advice from specialists or from the anode manufacturers should be sought as to the required size of anodes and exactly where to put them as there is the danger of overprotection by a too-large anode resulting in paint stripping.

CONTROL AND PREVENTION

Small yachts often have mild steel keels either in rectangular section bar form, or of thick plate. The same comments apply to mild steel keels as to those of cast iron.

The problem of keel bolts is common to both cast iron and steel keels; it is a ticklish problem because iron and steel are low in the galvanic series and there is no close 'non-corrodible' metal that would do as a keel bolt. Aluminium alloy is *less* noble and would corrode galvanically in no time; also the marine grades are relatively weak. The copper alloys are all galvanically incompatible with iron and steel: for example, if bronze bolts were used what would happen is that the bolts would be protected but the holes in the iron would enlarge rather rapidly. Although it is seldom done, it is possible to insulate the bolt with a hard plastic washer and sleeve. The seawater resistant copper alloys could then be used e.g. silicon bronze, nickel-aluminium bronze and gunmetal. Epoxy or nylon dipping might also be considered as double security against galvanic corrosion, although the trouble with any coating on the long bolts is that it is likely to be scuffed badly as the bolt is driven home. Coating the *noble* items (the keel bolts) is far preferable as a means of avoiding a galvanic cell than coating the iron and leaving the bolt bare because of the area ratio effect if the coating is damaged.

Common practice is to use mild steel bolts – a cheap and cheerful solution. Wrought iron was commonly used but in all probability it was no more satisfactory as far as rusting is concerned than mild steel. As discussed in Chapter 4 the corrosion rates of mild and low-alloy steels and the various grades of iron are all much the same. Mild steel is quite strong and is not prone to fail suddenly when used as a keel bolt material. Wastage will be gradual, and inevitable. Consequently a boat owner has to face up to the arduous task of withdrawing and inspecting the bolts at intervals.

Keel bolts are usually very long and of large diameter and rust may well have locked them in place. Removal often calls for a heavy maul and a great deal of effort, quite apart from the need to dig a pit under the keel in way of the bolts. There is no need to inspect every keel bolt at a time; two different ones every two years or so will give a good enough guide as to the situation. Rust bleeding from the interface between the hull and keel is a bad sign. Massive rusting can sometimes force the two apart. A loose keel is a very sure sign of trouble: not many yachts have actually dropped their keels but it does happen, sometimes with disastrous effects.

Mild steel keel bolts often 'waist' at the junction between the keel and the hull. Presumably water works its way into this area; in a timber hull the wood will be damp – just the conditions for severe rusting. Within the iron keel itself rust will seal the gaps and exclude oxygen.

Fortunately, today it is possible to have steel keel bolts radiographed (X-rayed) while in position thus saving the fruitless task of extracting *good* keel bolts. This technique is limited to ferrous bolts: copper alloys do not usually fail through waisting so imminent failure is less likely to be detected. Although ferrous bolts (steel and stainless steel) show up very well on X-rays if they are corroded and waisted, brass or bronze bolts in a lead keel (or any other keel for that matter) cannot be checked by this means because dezincification can take place without altering the apparent shape.

How can mild steel bolts be protected to prolong their lives? Galvanizing is well worth while, although with the large area of bare iron around the galvanizing is likely to act as a sacrificial anode. It is also worth painting the galvanizing, but again the paint will inevitably be scraped off when the bolt is driven home. So too would any soft coating over bare steel. Carefully aligning the holes and drilling them slightly oversize can overcome this problem. Such new techniques as epoxy or nylon dipping can then be employed. These very effective coatings can be a complete solution. The fact that the bolts will be a sloppy fit will not matter providing there is compression, between the ballast keel and the hull to prevent sideways movement. Yearly tightening of the bolts is indicated especially in a wooden boat where the timber around the bolt washer can crush in time.

There are all sorts of preserving oils and greases available, apart from plain bitumen or hot pitch, but in all probability they have a short life. It is more profitable to try to keep the water away from the bolt with an excess of non-hardening sealant compound. Most cast iron keels are left 'as cast' and not machined or ground off where they meet the hull. Consequently there are gaps for water to enter. A sealing compound will have more chance of success if the keel is a close fit on the hull.

Leaving aside mild steel and copper alloys, the alloys that are galvanically relatively inert can be considered. These include stain-less steel, Monel and titanium. Monel and titanium would be very reliable but expensive; some authorities would not recommend them because they might cause enlargement of the holes in the cast iron, but not to such an extent as would a copper alloy. Again, coating the bolt, or better, electrically insulating it, would be good practice.

Stainless steel keel bolts are commonly used in fibreglass yachts. Knowing the tendency for stainless to pit underwater, and for the lesser grades to stress corrosion cracking, one would think that it was the last alloy to use. But the reality is not so gloomy.

Providing a chromium-nickel-molybdenum alloy is used (Type 316) and that every effort is made to keep water away from the bolts by the use of sealant, and providing the hull is of fibreglass and not timber, service performance seems quite good. The fact that the stainless is surrounded and cathodically protected by a large mass of iron must help. Again, the bolt does not pass through wet wood, which alleviates the problem of crevice corrosion. Lloyds allow Type 316 stainless steel keel bolts for an iron keel. Nevertheless regular withdrawal is still necessary if one is to be fully confident at sea in a blow.

Lead Keels

A lead keel costs far more than an iron or steel one but is better in terms of density, lack of corrosion and easy compatibility with copper alloy bolts. Lead is fairly inert galvanically and it is ac-ceptable for the bolt material to be slightly *less* noble, e.g. gun-metal, silicon bronze or copper-nickel. It is obviously better to use a more noble alloy such as nickel-aluminium-bronze, Monel or one of the super alloys such as alloy 625 or titanium. Price and availability usually narrow the field to nickel-aluminium-bronze, gunmetal or silicon bronze – all perfectly acceptable and likely to have a long life. The interval between withdrawal can be far longer than with an iron keel: not only a convenience but also a con-fidence-booster!

Concrete keels pose different problems. They must be suf-ficiently strong in themselves to take load without cracking so internal steel reinforcement is necessary, quite apart from the need to fill the mix with scrap metal to increase its overall density. Even so the density of such a concrete keel is considerably less than iron. However, nowadays iron 'shot' – particles of spherical and angular cast iron – is available, which in a carefully controlled mix can produce a ballast material 75% as dense as iron.

In either case the reinforcing bars should be well covered by concrete to avoid rusting: at least ¾ in. (20 mm) in from the surface. The keel bolts can be of mild steel or a copper alloy providing the bolt holes are well away from the steel reinforcement throughout their length. Even so it is well to coat the bolts beforehand. Stainless steel bolts (Type 316) are also a possibility. The alkaline conditions help to prevent crevice corrosion.

Choice of Keel Bolt Material

Iron Keel: Mild steel: short life

Stainless steel: Type 316 and use plenty of bedding compound

Gunmetal, silicon bronze, aluminium bronze, or better nickel-aluminium-bronze, Monel: good electrical insulation should be arranged for any of these alloys

Titanium – if available

Lead keel: Silicon bronze, gunmetal, aluminium bronze, or better nickel-aluminium-bronze, Monel or any 'super' alloy including titanium

Lloyds recommend galvanized iron or steel and stainless steel (Cr/Ni/Mo type) for an iron keel, and bronze (gunmetal, silicon bronze, aluminium bronze and Monel) for a lead keel.

Whatever the keel material avoid using any type of brass, manganese bronze or aluminium for the keel bolts. Copper, while very compatible with lead makes a weak fastening although actually it is little weaker than gunmetal.

Since the strength of the keel bolting arrangement is so vital, it is wise to be very generous when deciding on the number and diameter of the bolts. The actual loads on a keel bolt when

143

grounding or when pounding at sea are incalculable but the static load is quite simply obtained. The factor of safety on the tensile strength of the bolt relative to this *static* load should be very large: in the order of 30. In other words the normal load – the weight each bolt holds – should be only one-thirtieth of the breaking load. That figure is a starting point in choosing the diameter.

Since a thin bolt corrodes through in a shorter time than a thick bolt, it makes sense to have fewer large bolts rather than a large number of thin ones. On the other hand, to rely on say only two bolts is taking this idea too far. So the minimum number is about five, always providing the hull itself is strong enough local to each bolt to take the higher load.

Keel bolts should be staggered from side to side of the thickness of the keel and not run in a line along the centre. This arrangement resists sideways loads better (26).

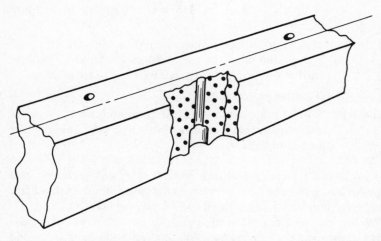

(26) Keel bolts should be staggered rather than on the centreline. A corrosion resistant bolt material will give more confidence for a greater number of years before its withdrawal becomes necessary. Anything which makes the awful task of withdrawing keel bolts easier should be considered. With cast iron keels the heads can be heavily recessed thus shortening the bolt: there is then less length to seize with rust and the withdrawal space needed under the keel is less.

Internal Ballast

Here it is just a question of resisting rust, if cast iron blocks ('pig iron') are used. Lead blocks are obviously better.

Galvanizing is possible, but galvanizers often require the pigs to be heavily shot-blasted to remove sand and other inclusions which can cause trouble in the bath. Zinc spraying is a good alternative, epoxy or nylon dipping two more. Most people simply accept the chore of wire-brushing and painting every few years. Heat-sealing the pigs in heavy gauge plastic bags after covering them with a rust-inhibiting oil is another trick.

Sterngear

Since the stern tube, propeller shaft, propeller and shaft bracket may well be in electrical contact with one another, it is necessary to make sure they are galvanically compatible by checking the chosen alloys against the galvanic series. The following takes these items one by one.

Propeller Shafts

Like keel bolts, propeller shafts pose considerable difficulties. The best materials are expensive. Manganese bronze used to be the normal choice but it tends to wear quite rapidly and is subject to dezincification. The tendency to dezincify is much less if the shaft is cathodically protected as it would be if electrically linked to a steel hull or if zinc sacrificial collars are fitted onto the shaft. Manganese bronze shafts on steel boats are generally satisfactory in seawater. Manganese bronze is satisfactory in fresh water.

Today stainless steel is more commonly used on fibreglass craft, but although harder wearing the problem with stainless is crevice corrosion. Barnacles sticking to the shaft create ideal conditions for pitting; so do rubber bearings and many shafts have become badly pitted in way of rubber bearings. While the shaft is stationary the rectangular areas of the rubber fluting pressing against the shaft starve the metal of oxygen and pits can quickly form (27). When

CONTROL AND PREVENTION

(27) Pitting on a stainless steel shaft is most likely to occur where the fluting of a water-lubricated rubber bearing presses against the shaft when the boat is idle.

the shaft turns again the rubber is torn. Pitting can also occur on the taper or in the propeller nut thread.

Obviously higher grade stainless steels make better shafts. Type 316 is the normal 'best' although some proprietary stainless steels with a higher alloy content are even better. Only by knowing the composition can one judge how far up the 'scale' the alloy is.

Cathodic protection reduces the tendency to pit so the deliberate attachment of sacrificial zinc anodes to the shaft is worth while. Rotating the shaft a few turns every week when the boat is afloat, but idle, is also a good idea. To avoid crevices in the taper and the thread a good fit and the use of a thread sealant or waterproof grease are advisable (28). Even with all these precautions there is no guarantee that pitting will not occur on a Type 316 shaft. Higher-alloy grades of stainless steel shafting when available may solve the problem in the future. Lower-alloy grades of stainless in seawater – even Type 304 – are very prone to pitting. In clean fresh water, however, Type 304 should give very good service, even without the precautions of cathodic protection, etc.

Whatever the shaft material never use a graphite-based grease in a metal bearing because graphite is so noble. Similarly, never use graphite impregnated packing.

146

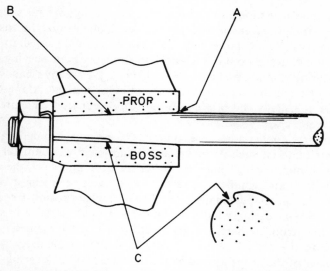

(28) Beware of pitting of stainless steel shafts around the propeller. Ensure a close fit on the taper and avoid bell-mouthing as at A, and rough machining marks as at B. Use copious sealant when assembling. Keyways cause stress concentrations and to minimize these they should have a 'sledge ending' and fillet radii rather than sharp corners as at C.

A final point on the subject of stainless shafts is that if the stern tube is particularly long or has a metal outer bearing, seawater in the tube will be stagnant thus encouraging crevice corrosion. In such cases it is good practice to pass part of the engine coolant into the stern tube or make some arrangement to circulate the outside water through the tube.

Monel shafting is commonly available but not so popular because of its price. The tendency to pit is far less, although it has been known. Monel Alloy 400 is strong; Monel Alloy K500 twice as strong.

Even more expensive would be titanium. Only a very few craft such as naval craft and hydrofoils have employed titanium.

Back to earth again, mild steel can give a reasonable life in seawater if protected. In way of the bearing the shaft must be sleeved with bronze and elsewhere a coating of some sort must be applied especially where the shaft is inaccessible. The coating is often glassfibre tape and resin but epoxy coatings are possible. A higher strength steel will allow a smaller diameter but the rusting problem will be much the same. In fresh water mild steel shafts are quite popular and even last a reasonable time without sleeving, but the bearing should also be of steel otherwise even really clean water will cause galvanic activity in such intimate contact. Manganese bronze is usually the best compromise between cost and life for fresh water craft, however.

Zinc-free copper alloys are sometimes used on seagoing boats as a shaft material such as nickel-aluminium-bronze, gunmetal and silicon bronze. Being somewhat softer than stainless steel, the wear rate is high and gunmetal is rather weak hence requiring a larger diameter. But all these materials will give a long corrosion-free life.

When considering what shaft material to choose bear in mind that the stronger materials might allow a smaller diameter thus reducing the cost. There is usually a minimum dictated by the diameter of the propeller and by the distance between bearings, but Monel and stainless are stronger than mild steel or manganese bronze. Subject to the bearing spacing, the factors are: for manganese bronze and mild steel shafts of 1 in. diameter, a Type 316 stainless shaft can be 0.95 in. and Monel K500 0.81 in.

Nowadays there are techniques for restoring worn shafts, i.e. worn rather than dezincified. The shaft can be built up by a spiral weld and then machined. The weld metal must be identical to or more noble than the parent metal. This technique can also be used to provide a tough corrosion resistant coating, for instance of stainless steel or Monel on a mild steel shaft. These processes are well established and normally cost less than buying a new shaft.

See Appendix for an example of a proprietary stainless material.

Propellers

Manganese bronze is perhaps the most widely used alloy for propellers: it is relatively inexpensive, easily repaired and reasonably strong. Since it is not actually a bronze but a brass, it is liable to dezincification. Zinc anodes mounted on the shaft or bolted on the hull and electrically coupled to the shaft will more or less control this type of corrosion. A manganese bronze propeller on a steel hull is also protected.

Gunmetal is virtually corrosion proof but is weak, which therefore requires thicker blades. This in turn leads to a loss of propeller efficiency, although the loss is only 1–2% for slow-speed boats and unnoticeable.

Steel and iron propellers are cheap but not often used. Obviously a bare steel or iron propeller has a short life: a fast water flow over the blades and cavitation attack tends to strip off any paint or metal coating after which the underlying steel begins to rust. Although it is not often done, galvanizing or zinc spraying and then epoxy dipping should give a long life on pleasure boats which run no more than one or two hundred hours a year under power. However, in the case of planing boats, where cavitation can be severe, any relatively soft coatings are liable to be stripped off a propeller.

Aluminium is universally used for outboard and outdrive propellers, mainly to achieve galvanic compatibility with the leg which is also aluminium, although outboard and propeller manufacturers do offer stainless and bronze alternatives. Normally the rubber hub electrically isolates the propeller, but it is best to tilt the leg out of the water if possible when the boat is idle. Stainless steel and bronze propellers allow thinner and more efficient blades but the increase in boat performance only becomes measurable on fast runabouts and then only at speeds well over 30 knots. For general purposes the aluminium propellers (usually coated, with epoxy for instance) give good performance and a long corrosion-free life.

Returning to inboard engines, apart from manganese bronze, steel and gunmetal other available propeller materials include stainless steel and nickel-aluminium-bronze. Type 304 stainless is commonly used in the USA for tugs and gives good and readily-repairable service. Since such boats are in regular use pitting is less likely. On a pleasure boat which spends much of its time static, stainless is not such a good idea. Nickel-aluminium-bronze or gunmetal are virtually corrosion-free and probably no more expensive than stainless steel.

Cavitation corrosion is a problem on fast-revving highly loaded propellers – typically on heavy planing cruisers – and Chapter 6 on Velocity Effects gives a 'grading' for the various propeller materials.

CONTROL AND PREVENTION

Although some copper alloys such as copper-nickel resist fouling, their antifouling property falls off markedly as the copper content goes below about 60% or 70%. Thus while nickel-aluminium-bronze and gunmetal propellers will resist fouling, manganese bronze is not very toxic to marine life and the decision whether to paint the propeller with antifouling is borderline. Monel, stainless steel, mild steel and aluminium have no anti-fouling properties. If any copper alloy propeller is cathodically protected then its anti-fouling property will disappear.

Sterntubes and Shaft Struts

The sterntube is a round tube with at each end a bearing set in a housing. A flange is cast as part of the after housing, usually with two screw or bolt holes, to fix the whole assembly to the hull. A brass or a bronze is generally used. Often the tube is brass and so is the shell of the rubber bearing. The cast housings are often gun-metal. Clearly brass should be avoided if at all possible, but if it is used then the fitting of sacrificial zinc anodes is advisable to reduce the tendency to dezincification. The tube is sometimes quoted as 'a BS 249 sterntube', implying that it is to the highest marine quality. But like so many references to British Standard Specifications, this one is not a marine standard (which has a prefix MA) nor does the standard specify a material that is resistant to seawater (BS 249 used to refer to leaded 60/40 brass but is now withdrawn). Brass sterntubes are of course very acceptable for fresh water craft.

Cathodic protection is often a palliative measure fitted to over-come dezincification problems caused by fitting cheap brass and manganese bronze sterngear. Although protection is given, on a wooden boat there is a strong chance of alkaline attack of the adjacent timbers over a period of years. This attack, which causes the wood to go soft, often occurs around the sterntube or shaft bracket since they represent the largest lumps of metal in contact with the hull. The timbers in this area are difficult to replace so it pays to follow the recommendation in Chapter 9 on Cathodic Protection.

However, consider the simple principle that if corrosion resistant metals are used in the first place cathodic protection is not necessary. In other words, avoid brass, manganese bronze and stainless steel for the sterngear and instead use gunmetal for the sterntube, shaft bracket and propeller. And if the shaft must be of stainless or manganese bronze then fit shaft anodes and rubber bearings so that the sterntube is electrically isolated and not therefore cathodically protected. Only protect the items that need protection. The problem of alkali attack via cathodic protection does not of course apply with fibreglass boats, although paint detachment has been known to take place.

Seacocks

Many a boat has sunk quietly at her moorings because of a slow water leak caused by a faulty seacock or its fastening bolts because brass or manganese bronze has been used. And this applies to any skin fittings below the waterline: cockpit drains, sink outlets, etc. The common brass gate valve that plumbers use has no place on board a seagoing boat, although such valves are satisfactory in the fresh drinking water system on board, or on a clean-freshwater craft.

The whole seacock must be of salt water resistant metal: it is no use having the body of bronze and the threaded screw shaft brass because the thread will dezincify (especially as brass is *less* noble than bronze) and one day the handle will just keep turning without moving the gate.

Unfortunately chandlers' catalogues often list both brass and gunmetal (or aluminium bronze) seacocks without mentioning that each has its specific use. Particularly misleading are taper plug type seacocks, with a flange obviously intended to be bolted to the hull, blithely described as 'all brass'. Just as misleading are the set of four seacock bolts specified as 'manganese bronze' – an absolutely disastrous combination on a saltwater boat. After a few years the seacock could come loose or fall to bits and water flood into the hull. Amazing material combinations are often described quite clearly under the heading 'inlet seacock', such as 'manganese bronze hull fitting; gunmetal gate valves'.

For peace of mind, make sure that seacocks or any underwater inlet or outlet are made of gunmetal, silicon bronze or aluminium bronze (for recommendations on metal hulls see Chapter 12). Even aluminium bronze has a slight tendency to de-alloy. Nickel-aluminium-bronze is safer. Similarly, always use bolts of these metals: never brass or manganese bronze. (Remember also that 'naval brass' is only a version of common 60/40 type brass.)

A gate valve stamped 'BS 1952' is no guarantee of seawater resistant materials. This standard is mainly concerned with pressure and temperature ratings of gate valves made of different materials, including brass.

Apart from using brass or manganese bronze, seacock manufacturers can also be criticized for leaving protruding edges on the inside which are prone to create blockages. This applies particularly to taper plug valves, particularly ones for toilet outlets. Often the hole in the taper plug does not line up with the outlet hole. However, a burr cutter in an electric drill will soon rectify this defect. A third point for criticism concerns the bolts holding on the flange which in turn holds on the taper plug. If the nuts of these bolts come loose through vibration a serious leak into the boat can be expected. Locking tab washers rather than the less reliable spring washers ought to be provided, but rarely are.

Rudders and Rudder Pintles

Mild steel plate rudders are cheap and convenient to make. On the other hand they are not the best hydrodynamic shape, and if they are too large to be galvanized they rust. Bare plate painted ones are ideal candidates for sacrificial anode protection. Large rudders are better zinc sprayed and painted.

Steel pintles even if galvanized will quickly rust where the bearing action wears off the coating, so here is a typical case where changing to a better metal for a small extra cost can save much time and trouble later on. Stainless steel is particularly good for this application if the pintles are above water, but most such items on the market are fabricated from thin plate and do not look very strong. Massive cast stainless pintles would be better. Brass, bronze or manganese bronze ones are also likely to give good service above water. Underwater, one ought to avoid brass or manganese bronze. Stainless steel ones (for underwater use) should be of Type 316 and the owner would be advised to keep a regular check for pitting. The pin and the fixing bolts are particularly at risk: bolts of Monel would be more reliable.

Fast motor cruisers often have spade rudders made of stainless steel with an integral stainless stock. The bearing should be of bronze. The rudder blade itself if antifouled is unlikely to become pitted, but the stock, especially at the lower end and at the point of greatest stress, is prone, and a wise owner will drop the rudder during lay-up time and inspect the stock for pitting.

Outboards and outdrives are sometimes fitted with small rudders clamped to the leg to help steering at low speeds. These rudders should be of a marine grade of aluminium and fastened with Type 316 stainless bolts. Since the leg is aluminium it is essential to avoid any copper alloy or even steel. Galvanized steel would be satisfactory, however.

Centreboards

Most centreboards are of mild steel, sometimes galvanized sometimes not. That in itself does not produce special problems but the pivot bolt and the hoisting gear often enhance corrosion. The bearing areas in way of both the pivot bolt and the lifting tackle are especially prone to a vigorous corrosion. The actual surfaces in contact rub together and are immersed in salt water. Any galvanizing or other protective coating soon rubs off exposing the bare steel edge. The hole in the centreplate then enlarges quickly. The lifting tackle pin is necessarily close to the edge of the plate and eventually after a few seasons can pull through the edge releasing the centreplate. This process will happen even with compatible metals – in most cases a galvanized shackle pin in a steel centreboard – but if a stainless or bronze shackle is used the rate of corrosion of the hole is many times faster because of galvanic effects.

With a mild steel centreboard there is no long-lasting solution to this problem except to use compatible materials, i.e. a galvanized shackle on the end of the lifting wire and a galvanized pivot bolt, and then to accept that steady wear will take place. Each year the items should be inspected and replaced when necessary.

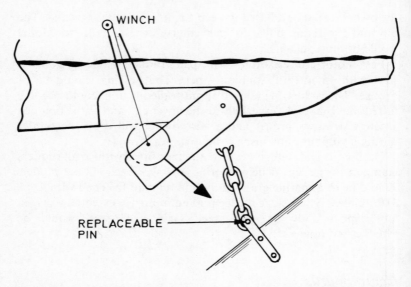

(29) Steel centreboards pose corrosion problems at the pivot bolt and lifting point. Chain and replacable wear pin are preferable to a wire rope shackled directly into a hole in the plate.

In the case of the lifting tackle at least the wear of the plate itself can easily be avoided by fitting a pair of mild steel straps and having a replaceable pin (29). With more difficulty, the hole for the pivot bolt can be fitted with a removable steel bush. Then at least all the wearing parts are easily replaced.

Obviously the thicker the bolt and the pin the longer their life; many boats with centreboards are fitted with pathetically thin pivot bolts which while being quite strong enough when new can tolerate very little corrosion.

The lifting wire itself is a problem. Constantly wetted, neither galvanized nor stainless wire is likely to last long. Stainless wire will give a short life underwater because of pitting, and if a copper-sleeved Talurit splice is fitted this will corrode preferentially. Polyester (Terylene or Dacron) rope is one solution, though with a chafe problem, but galvanized chain is better. The lowest link will take the wear but if an overlong piece of chain is fitted in the first place it can be cut off in due course and the next link up used in-

154

stead. The galvanizing will last only a few years so replacement of the chain must be considered as a matter of course.

A complete long-lasting solution to the wear problem at the pivot and lifting pin on a steel centreplate is elusive. Obviously a longer life would ensue if the wearing areas were of a hard and corrosion resistant metal: this suggests stainless steel. The pitting problem would be reduced by the cathodic protection given by the steel plate. So, at the pivot, one would end up with a stainless bush fixed to the plate and with a stainless steel bolt, making sure that Type 316 stainless steel was used. The bush could be rivetted, bolted or even welded in place. Similarly the lifting point could be bushed, or stainless steel tangs could be fitted. From there a stainless shackle would lead to a polyester lifting rope.

Of course a centreboard of zinc-free copper alloy would solve all the problems because the attachments could then be of the same corrosion-free alloys. Suitable metals that come to mind are copper, gunmetal and copper-nickel. Copper alloys are much the same density or a little heavier than steel. A bonus would be that no antifouling would be necessary. The lifting wire could be of Monel (which is available, though at a price). Stainless steel for the centreplate could also be considered (again Type 316) with sacrificial anodes.

Usually cost rules out such materials and mild steel is the only practical choice; but to avoid disaster it is wise to consider carefully the pivot and lifting arrangements.

Fastenings

Corrosion problems underwater are often associated with fastenings. Brass screws and bolts are often the culprits, but stainless steel fastenings also give trouble.

There are two distinct problem areas: (a) where the fastening holds together non-metallic items, e.g. wood to wood or wood to fibreglass; (b) where it holds a metal item in place, e.g. a seacock in a fibreglass hull. Taking the first case, clearly all that is required is a corrosion resistant alloy. In this category are:

> Copper (boat nails and clenches)
> Silicon bronze
> Aluminium bronze (very slight chance of de-alloying)
> Nickel-aluminium-bronze (NAB)
> Gunmetal
> Copper-nickel
> Monel (very slight chance of pitting)
> Nickel-chromium alloys (Inconel, Inculoy)
> Titanium

Of these only copper, silicon bronze and to a lesser extent Monel and aluminium bronze are normally available through chandlers. Silicon bronze is used for barb-ring nails; gunmetal fasteners need to be of ample diameter to compensate for the lower strength of the alloy.

In the less corrosion resistant category come:

> 'Anodic coated' steel and iron
> Stainless steel
> Brass
> Manganese bronze

Brass and manganese bronze should be avoided like the plague. Dezincification and complete failure are most likely in seawater. Stainless steel fastenings without the cathodic protection afforded by a surrounding mass of less noble metal are also to be avoided. Stainless screws and bolts tend to pit badly in seawater especially in the crevices caused by threads and under their washers or heads. Attack is severe in wet wood.

'Anodic coated' steel and iron fastenings embrace galvanized, electroplated zinc or cadmium, and sherardized. For underwater use only hot-dip galvanized fastenings should ever be used because galvanizing gives the greatest thickness of zinc coating. Even so the life of the coating before rusting starts is very variable, depending mainly on whether the zinc coating is constantly wet or not.

In the case of galvanized bolts, before buying check that the thread is also galvanized and has not been cut *after* the galvanizing process.

Chandlers usually stock only brass and stainless steel, both being very unsuitable for underwater fastenings. The grade of stainless is rarely mentioned and is often only Type 304. The brass fasteners are usually only 60/40 brass and not inhibited: again totally unsuitable for use underwater. Thus the boat owner has great difficulty in obtaining seawater resistant fasteners, though for fresh water use he is better off because he can expect a reasonable life from either of these alloys providing the water is not polluted.

Where the fastening is not in isolation but is holding a metal item in position, galvanic effects have to be taken into consideration. The correct principle is to make sure that the fastening metal is the same or slightly more noble than the fitting (see Chapter 7). Table 12 gives a guide as to which fastener metal to use. Common combinations are:

Fitting	*Correct fasteners*
Aluminium bronze seacock	Aluminium bronze or silicon bronze
Gunmetal sterntube	Silicon bronze or NAB
Stainless steel	Monel
Aluminium outdrive	Stainless steel Type 316
Galvanized steel stem band	Galvanized steel

Generally, stainless steel fasteners should not be used underwater. However they *are* used quite frequently, but only if all of the following conditions are met will they be satisfactory:

(a) Austenitic grade at least Type 304, preferably Type 316.

(b) Not passing through wet wood.

(c) Ample sealant under the head and in between mating surfaces.

(d) The item to be fastened is less noble than stainless; i.e. all the copper alloys and, with some risk of hole enlargement, steel and iron.

Condition (b) indicates that stainless wood *screws* must never be used underwater.

Outdrives and Outboards

Since the major components of these are of aluminium alloy care has to be taken to avoid galvanic action to the detriment of the aluminium.

CONTROL AND PREVENTION

(a) Never use a copper-based antifouling on the hull or outdrive.

(b) Use stainless steel bolts to mount the outdrive transom pad.

(c) Never use copper alloys in contact with the outdrive or outboard (if adding a rudder, for instance).

(d) On a wooden or even fibreglass hull ensure that there are no copper alloy fittings or fasteners in close proximity to the aluminium, i.e. less than a foot or two (30–60 cm). If there are, coat the exposed copper alloy with an epoxy paint.

(d) Make sure there is no devious electrical path to a more noble item, e.g. a bronze seacock. (The electrical path being for instance via the engine cooling water pipes and the drive shaft.)

(f) Beware electrolytic action; a current flow from the boat's battery or shore supply grounding into the water through the outdrive or outboard. The best way to do this is to ensure that there is no continuous electrical path to the unit via the drive shaft, control cables or mounting bolts.

(g) Replace the zinc anodes usually fitted to outdrives and outboards when they are almost eaten away.

Antifoulings

Environmental concerns are rapidly causing the ingredients in antifouling paints to change. Many types employ a high copper content and are therefore unsuitable for coating aluminium outdrives or hulls. Check the paint manufacturer's application notes before using.

Chapter 11
Problem Areas on Deck and Aloft

Bollards, Fairleads, etc

A multitude of different metal items are found on deck: stem fittings, winches, cleats, lead blocks, ventilators, etc. Metal fittings not only need to be corrosion resistant but also need to keep their smart appearance. The degree of corrosion resistance necessary is essentially to do with surface corrosion. Unlike the situation underwater, brass and manganese bronze are fine on deck, but the trouble with any copper alloy is that the surface tarnishes to a greeny-brown colour. Hence the attraction of chromium plate, but unfortunately the quality of the majority of chrome plated marine hardware is too low to last for very many seasons on deck. Plating to a high standard (e.g. BS 1224 Grade 1C or ISO 1456–8) is necessary to achieve a reasonable life on deck. I have never had a chromium plated fitting on deck where the chrome has lasted for more than a season or two before either crazing or peeling has occurred, and now prefer to have bare manganese bronze or gunmetal. Gunmetal is the weaker of these materials and the casting needs to be of substantial thickness. With any chrome-plated item, one is really buying for the underlying material: plating soon wears off fairleads, cleats, locks and hasps, especially on edges.

The following is a list of commonly used alloys all of which will give a long life on deck although the surface may tarnish:

Deck fitting	Fastening
Brass	Brass
Manganese bronze	Brass
Gunmetal	Brass

Aluminium alloy	Stainless (ideally insulated)
Galvanized steel	Galvanized (or stainless)
Stainless steel	Stainless

Hot-dip galvanizing is the best coating for steel; avoid electro-plating or sherardizing. Unpainted, a galvanized fitting will last ten years or so on deck without rust appearing, provided the zinc coating is not rubbed off by a rope or chain lying in a fairlead, for example.

Aluminium alloy fittings are light and strong. Unanodised, they will soon go spotty. Again, if anything rubs against an anodised surface the bare metal will soon be exposed. Only the appearance will suffer; so long as a marine grade is used no serious corrosion will take place.

Stainless fittings are ideal, especially those which are cast rather than fabricated and welded from bits of tube and plate. Type 304 will give very good service on deck on a salt water craft but rust staining is inevitable. Type 316 is better from this point of view. Inland, Type 304 should remain 'stainless'.

Always use copious flexible bedding compound to keep water off the fastenings (stainless or brass) particularly if they go through wood. A belt-and-braces man would shun brass and try to obtain silicon bronze fastenings instead.

Galvanized fittings pose a problem if galvanized screws are unobtainable. The second practical choice is stainless. Local activity can be expected, in that the screw will become covered with a zinc deposit. After that the action should stop. This also happens with brass screws in galvanized fittings. As always, if dissimilar metals are used it is essential that the fastener is more noble than the fitting.

Pulpits, Stanchions and Lifelines

Three metals are usually used: stainless steel, galvanized steel and aluminium alloy. A boat owner can easily fabricate pulpits and stanchions himself from galvanized steel tube and then have the welded parts re-galvanized afterwards. Actually, many seasons of rust-free life are given simply by painting the welded areas with a zinc-rich paint and then the whole item with a paint scheme suitable for zinc. Anodised aluminum or stainless steel pulpits and stanchions keep their appearance for a long time without paint, of course. Previous comments about marine grade aluminium and Type 304 and 316 stainless also apply here, and also the comments on fastenings. Because of its shape, regular cleaning of aluminium or stainless tubing is easy and worth doing to retain the bright appearance. Proprietary cleaners are available.

Where the pulpit or stanchions are bolted to a metal deck the appropriate measures must be taken to avoid galvanic activity. For instance, with stainless stanchions on an aluminium deck it is very desirable to insulate the two by fitting a gasket of say Tufnol. The foot of a stanchion is often an area where puddles of water can lie and since the security of stanchions is so important it is very wise to insulate.

Wire lifelines are generally either galvanized or stainless, and sometimes plastic covered. The plastic covering inevitably stops just short of the swaged and or Talurit splice and water gets in just at the place where the wire would break anyway. Plastic covered wire can therefore be a menace. Pre-stretched polyester is an attractive alternative as it will have a more comfortable diameter and be immune to corrosion. (Chafe is the only enemy, though; protective grommets in stanchions will help.)

Ground Tackle

Anchor chain on boats is invariably galvanized, though stainless anchors are now available as an expensive alternative to galvanized ones. Re-galvanizing after rusting appears is possible. Avoid any copper alloy items in the chain locker: if a perforated bottom is fitted to allow drainage, use wood, galvanized sheet or painted aluminium sheet. The navel pipe (chain pipe) from the deck into the chain locker is best made of galvanized steel or iron; aluminium is also compatible. Brass or bronze chain pipes are obviously not ideal but at least any corrosion of the chain is not hidden and should be noticed early on.

Window Frames

Anodised aluminium frames are very popular. The grade of anodising should be checked before buying and only a grade intended for marine use should be chosen (see Chapter 3 on Aluminium). Caravan windows are only given a thin anodising coating which soon succumbs to a salty environment.

Controls and Instruments

Invariably these are chromium plated. Exposed in the cockpit, the plating on the popular makes soon deteriorates, and even under shelter parts which are not regularly handled become irreparably pitted. These comments apply to gear levers, steering wheels and instrument bezels.

Davits

Metal davits are usually stainless steel, aluminium or mild steel, the latter two often being coated in nylon, polyurethene or epoxy (dipped rather than painted on). The finish lasts very well except where the coating is damaged. This can happen around the mounting bolts when the davits are installed or of course from chafe, knocks or accident. A galvanized and painted treatment would have slightly less 'showroom finish' but would be more robust and rust-free.

Hinges, Padlocks, Hasps and Staples

Beware of brass hinges with steel pins: the marine sort should have brass pins. An all-brass padlock (including the shackle) and hasp is all too easy for the thief to cut through. Hardened steel will rust. A stainless steel shackle and hasp is a compromise answer because it will be harder to cut through.

Problem Areas Aloft

Masts

Aluminium masts should of course be made of a marine grade aluminium (often 6082 or HE 30) and heavily anodised (e.g. to BS 1615 AA 25). (Other relevant standards are given in Chapter 3.) Thereafter it is a matter of avoiding galvanic corrosion due to attaching more noble metals (especially copper alloys). The anodising will give no protection against this type of corrosion. Since aluminium is so low in the galvanic series most other metals will cause some corrosion, including all copper alloys, tin, lead, copper and even steel. The only metals that are relatively 'safe' are aluminium of course, galvanized steel, stainless steel and Monel. Rivets are best made of aluminium, stainless steel or Monel. A bronze winch for example must be insulated from the mast by mounting it on a Tufnol (or similar) pad which in turn is mounted on an aluminium seat rivetted to the mast (30). The bolts must also be insulated with non-conducting sleeves and washers to avoid electrical continuity. Use zince chromate paste on the faying surfaces and also in rivetted joints.

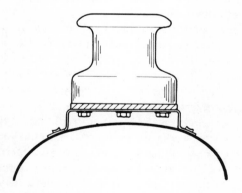

(30) A bronze winch must be insulated from an aluminium mast or deck by, for instance, a Tufnol pad. The stainless bolts should also be insulated with non-conducting sleeves and washers.

CONTROL AND PREVENTION

The choice of metals for the mast step should also take galvanic action into account. The heel pivot bolt should be stainless. If the mast sits on the keel make sure that it is well away from steel floors or bronze keel bolts. Where it goes through a wooden deck make sure that copper nails have not been used to fasten the mast coat nor brass screws to secure a collar to a wood deck. Wet wood can make an effective conductor of electricity, and balsa or foam cored sandwich construction can also hold water.

A galvanized tabernacle is suitable for an aluminium mast but make sure the pivot bolt is stainless or galvanized.

Chafe from a flapping halyard, or incorrectly led running rigging can wear away the anodizing.

Rigging

Wire rope is usually either galvanized or stainless. Nowadays stainless wire is more common and it does generally last a very long time. Galvanized wire rope should be a marine grade, that is to say more heavily galvanized than ordinary industrial wire rope. BS MA 29 'Yacht Ropes' refers to BS 2763 galvanized Class A. The life of a galvanized wire rope is more or less dictated by the thickness of the galvanizing since once rust has started on one or two strands they soon break and then the whole wire becomes suspect and must be replaced. Traditional annual preserving treatment called for soaking in a mixture of petrol, linseed oil and varnish, or paraffin and other concoctions. Anhydrous lanoline is also a good treatment, put on hot. The many modern penetrating spray preservatives – those that set to a gel – are no doubt beneficial. Prevention of accidental abrasion of the soft zinc is also an important contributor to long life.

Old catalogues and books often refer to 'plough' steel wire rope. This was galvanized steel wire rope as we know it today, but the term gave the impression that it was in some way superior especially as one could ask for 'Best Plough' or 'Extra Special Plough'. Nowadays the terms are embraced by a standard tensile strength, for example 145 Grade Steel to BS 302:1968, the rope being made up for example to BS 365:1968. The galvanizing should be to BS 2763.

164

Stainless wire rope must be of Type 316 stainless and nowadays this grade is more or less standard (at least in the UK) and is specified by BS MA 29 'Yacht Ropes'. In this standard the required strengths are slightly less than for galvanized wire of the same diameter.

Whereas the life of galvanized wire rope depends on the longevity of the zinc coating, the life of stainless is dictated more by fatigue and corrosion fatigue, pitting and stress corrosion. Failure is more likely at or near a terminal or at any item attached to the wire – or indeed anywhere where the lay of the rope has been kinked or disturbed. The undisturbed and exposed part of the wire will last almost indefinitely subject to fatigue.

The more flexible the construction of the wire the less the stress induced in the individual strands each time the rope is bent. Wire running rigging needs to be of a very flexible construction if it is to have a reasonable life running over sheaves; 7x19 is usually chosen compared to 7x7 for standing rigging, or 1x19 which is even stiffer and stronger.

Wire Terminals

Inevitably, terminals create problems. They distort the lay of the rope, in the process stressing some strands more than others. They create pockets where water can lie to cause pitting. And if the terminal is held rigidly the wire then is forced to flex close to the terminal which of course leads to fatigue.

The most usual types of terminal are: Talurit (squeezed-on metal sleeve), patent terminals which grip the strands over a cone, hand-splicing, and bulldog grips (U-shaped bolts with a saddle). All these, if properly made, should be approximately as strong as the rope.

Talurit splices are very neat and convenient. With galvanized wire rope they should be of aluminium and with stainless, copper. It would be fatal to mix this order up. When the top of the copper sleeve is wet at least the stainless wire is cathodically protected. This and the fact that the copper is really squeezed in hard around the strands means that pitting is not a problem.

Stainless patent terminals (for stainless wire only) should be

165

assembled with a sealant to prevent cavities where salt water would lie and cause pitting. They should also be unscrewed regularly and the condition of the outer strands of the wire checked where they are forced over the cone.

Hand splices are often parcelled for protection and to keep stray strand ends away from fingers. While this is satisfactory for galvanized wire, it is an invitation to pitting with stainless.

The humble bulldog grip is unsightly but cheap and reliable. They must be fitted correctly, i.e. three in number, with the saddle on the working part of the rope and not the tail end. They should be spaced about six rope diameters apart, and the one furthest from the eye should not be tightened too much.

Thimbles

A thimble in the eye is essential to prevent the wire from bending too sharply, which weakens it, disturbs the lay, and increases local stress. For stainless rope, the thimble should be made of stainless, brass or plastic (where the loads are not great). With galvanized wire obviously one must avoid these materials, except plastic, which may not be strong enough in any case. A galvanized steel thimble should be used on galvanized wire.

Rigging Screws (Bottle Screws or Turnbuckles)

These can be very much a problem area if the fitting chosen is undersized relative to the wire, of poor material, or badly designed or made. Failure usually occurs where the threaded shaft enters the body because this part usually has the least cross-sectional area of metal; also the fact that it is threaded causes violent stress concentrations. These two factors can be minimized by choosing the proper size of rigging screw for the wire.

What is not so obvious is that if the rigging screw has limited freedom to move at one or both ends it will be liable to fatigue. If the forked end is connected straight onto a shroud plate, for instance, it will only have complete freedom of movement fore and aft: the fork if it is at all close fitting will prevent much movement athwartships. Thus when someone pulls hard sideways on the stay the rigging screw will bend. Similarly if the eye terminal of the wire is connected straight into the fork of the screw, the flutter of the wire in a strong wind or a flogging headsail will continually flex the rigging screw. The weakest part of any rigging screw in sideways pull is undoubtedly the threaded shaft. Put a drop of seawater on the thread and expose it to fluctuating load from a vibrating wire and there we have a corrosion fatigue situation. The simple answer is to fit a toggle at top and bottom of the rigging screw and then it has freedom of movement in all directions (20).

Most rigging screws on the market can be criticized for their detail design. A cast body must never be used. Welding should be avoided especially in a stainless screw. Sometimes the threaded shaft is welded direct to the fork: one can easily see how well the weld has been machined or ground smooth but were precautions taken during manufacture against weld decay? Whatever the method of manufacture there is no excuse for using anything less than Type 316. Stress-raising, square-cut forks and bodies are also to be condemned. There is no reason why smoothly rounded parts cannot be produced. Never spring out a fork to fit an eye nor drill out an eye.

Vibration from wind or the engine can loosen a rigging screw, especially one well greased. Monel seizing wire is readily obtainable for stainless fittings; galvanized seizing wire should really be used for galvanized screws and shackles but in practice it does little harm to use Monel.

Steel and manganese bronze rigging screws are usually weaker than ones of stainless, which must be taken into account when choosing a size. Both types will fail from fatigue so toggles are still needed – and good design.

Shackles

Usually shackles fail because the pins bend or the U distorts, so *wide* shackles relative to the plate or eye that they enclose are unsuitable for high loads. Strip-metal shackles are particularly vulnerable.

Metals used are stainless steel, manganese bronze and galvanized steel. Perhaps due to the simplicity of a shackle's basic design, failures are rare and usually due to poor choice or fitting in such a way that it cants over (shackle too wide). Galvanized shackle pins tend to be self-seizing through corrosion in the thread, but nevertheless seizing wire is a wise precaution.

Naturally the shackle should be galvanically compatible with the fittings to which it is attached. Having said that, the worst combinations seem to cause only minor damage. Having studied many boats with mixed rigging arrangement (for instance a bronze shroud plate with galvanized shackle and stainless steel bottle screw) the worst that happens is that the galvanized item becomes locally corroded; the galvanizing is eaten off and the steel rusts underneath. But even this takes years to happen and is readily spotted and checked.

This situation is quite special: the contact is over a very small area, and for most of the time on a pleasure yacht, in temperate climate at least, the contact is either dry, or wet with rainwater rather than salt. The situation of a shackle in a centreboard fully immersed in *salt water* is markedly different. So too is galvanized wire rope in a brass or stainless thimble, because here the area of contact is continuous and the sacrificial item is thin strands of wire which can withstand very little depth of corrosion before they break under load.

Tangs and Chainplates

Since these are the vital attachment points to the boat and mast and are expected to last for the life of the boat, they must be several times stronger than the wire. There is no excuse for being mean with the size of these items. Tangs and shroud plates made of strip metal are of course open to fatigue failure. Only massive construction can overcome this basic design fault. They should be as short as possible to minimize the bending movement caused by side loads. Shroud plates made with an inverted U-shaped bolt are also suspect, especially if they protrude high off the deck. Eyebolts are more satisfactory from this point of view.

Some frightening masthead tang arrangements are seen on yachts: a conglomeration of bits of stainless strip and tube welded together. Long tangs are liable to fatigue exacerbated by a weld just at the root, while overlapping bits of metal can form water traps for pitting corrosion to take place. Of course Type 316 ought to be used, but so often who knows what grade it is.

When stainless fittings are used four possibilities ought to be kept in mind: pitting, fatigue, stress raisers (notches, sharp corners, etc) and weld decay.

The alternative as far as fittings for aluminium spars are concerned is galvanized steel. Compatibility with aluminium is theoretically better (though in practice the two ought to be separated by a neoprene gasket), while galvanized steel is less liable to fail without warning, is easier to weld (in the sense of getting a reliable weld), and is not subject to deep pitting. So galvanized steel fittings are in several ways better than stainless; however they are not so attractive nor so rust-free.

Chapter 12
Metal Hulls and Copper Sheathing

Steel Hulls

Since the oil crisis the price of fibreglass hulls has increased tremendously, which has led to renewed interest in the other boat-building materials particularly steel. Steel has also gained favour because today modern paints and the common use of blast-cleaning have much reduced the rust problem. Steel as a hull material has other attractions apart from low price: it does not leak and makes the strongest of hulls which will remain watertight even when run on the rocks. Mild steel yields almost like rubber and will deform rather than tear. A small steel hull is inevitably heavy, so only displacement speeds are normally possible.

Skin thickness is dictated by the need to avoid denting when coming alongside, taking the ground, or dishing caused by pounding at sea, and by the need to have a substantial 'corrosion allowance'. There are also the dictates of fabrication. Welding is difficult if the plate thickness is less than about 2 mm, and also, in general, the thicker the plate the less its distortion due to the heat of welding. Consequently plating is generally about $\frac{1}{4} - \frac{3}{16}$ in. (6–4 mm) for hulls and $\frac{1}{8}$ in. (2.5–3 mm) for cabins. (A hull thickness of 1 mm would be strong enough to resist the strains in a seaway, on a small boat, but framing would have to be very closely spaced to resist accidental denting, while corrosion would be the owner's nightmare. Such a hull would also be very difficult to build.)

The greater the amount of welding on a given area of plate the greater the likely distortion. Thus frameless construction is attractive. Distortion can be minimized by a skilled welding schedule and by heating and hammering after welding, and also by inter-

170

mittent welding of the frames to the skin. Fillers are often trowelled into hollow areas – not an ideal measure unless the hull is first blast-cleaned to create good adhesion.

Most hulls now are all-welded. The welded joint is as strong as the rest of the plate, providing good welding practice is used, and no extra corrosion problems are incurred. A welded seam will always rust first, however, simply because the paint film thickness becomes irregular over the weld bead. Ground flush, the overlying paint film will give equal protection, and rusting – when it starts – will begin at no particular place.

Rivetting as a method of constructing a hull has of course been proved over many years, but inevitably the plate edges and protruding rivet heads are places where rusting will start. Watertightness can be achieved either by putting a sealing composition between the mating surfaces before rivetting, or on thicker plate by the time-honoured method of caulking (using a pneumatic tool to split the edge of the plate and force half the thickness against the adjacent plate). Any slight initial rusting between the mating surfaces effectively seals the joint anyway, as oxygen is excluded. Poorly rivetted joints will rust badly, the rust in time forcing the joint apart.

Ordinary carbon steel (mild steel) is most commonly used. Low-alloy steels are favoured in certain quarters because they are claimed to be stronger and more corrosion resistant. Cor-Ten is one such low-alloy steel which is some 40% stronger (on yield strength), but costs around 40% more. Its extra corrosion resistance is debatable in the context of boat hulls.

Certainly above water a paint film on a low-alloy steel ought to last longer, while any rust in scratches ought not to creep under the surrounding paint film. But underwater the evidence suggests little improvement; indeed some tests have shown corrosion of bare Cor-Ten as slightly greater than that of bare mild steel. Consequently most people would not choose to pay the higher price for a small and dubious return, at least on corrosion grounds. Better to put the money into blast-cleaning and epoxy painting, inside and out. Nevertheless there are contrary opinions, notably in America where a low-alloy steel is often specified. The Royal National Lifeboat Institution in the UK also follows the trend with nineteen Cor-Ten lifeboats, though these are based on a U.S. specification.

CONTROL AND PREVENTION

Painting

Rust is certainly a big problem with a steel structure in a marine environment, but it is a problem that is tackled successfully by both ship and boat owners. Imagine the problem of maintaining the vast surface area, inside and out, of a large tanker: literally millions of square feet. A thin paint film is the steel's only protection and yet the majority of this area is kept rust-free for many years. Without modern paints huge oil tankers would be uneconomic. The owner of a small steel boat ought to take comfort in, and make use of, such paint technology.

Most paints prevent rusting by creating an impermeable barrier to the passage of galvanic currents. They have a high resistance to current flow even when immersed in water and thus prevent the setting up of tiny galvanic cells resulting from impurities on the surface of the steel. The success or otherwise of this 'resistance inhibition' depends on several factors.

THE THICKNESS OF THE PAINT FILM. There is a certain minimum thickness that will ensure success and this is in the order of 150–400 μm (6–16 mil), depending on the type of paint. Since this thickness cannot be achieved by a single coat it implies that several coats are needed especially if applied by brush. The number of coats is between four and seven, again depending on the type of paint.

SURFACE PREPARATION. This factor is the most critical of all. The surface of the steel must be clean, dry and free from grease and oil or any other contamination. Painting over a surface which is slightly damp or is covered in tiny pits each one full of hygroscopic rust or dirt particles will cause failure of the paint film in a very short time. Painting over rust seals in the ingredients of a galvanic cell and rust will continue to form underneath the paint which will soon crack open.

PAINTING CONDITIONS. When the steel is painted, the atmospheric conditions must be right. In general this implies painting only when the temperature is between 10° and 30°C with a relative humidity of less than 85%. In Britain these conditions are most likely to be achieved around noon and not later than about 6 p.m. in the summer months (2 p.m. in spring and autumn). Spring is more favourable than autumn since weather records show a higher chance of the right conditions occurring. Later in the day there is a chance of dew falling; night-time condensation will not be driven off until late morning since the temperature of the plate will lag behind that of the air: thus in general painting at noon is preferable. Of course painting inside a warm and dry shed is far better.

Surface Preparation

Millscale has been mentioned in Chapter 4 on Steel and Iron. This is the oxide crust formed during manufacture and it is 0.3 volts more noble than the underlying steel. Consequently it rapidly pits the plates if not completely removed before painting. But it is a tough scale and only blast-cleaning or power grinding will remove it. Common practice until the 1950s was to 'weather' the steel to remove the millscale. Plates were left outside for a few months and the subsequent rusting would loosen the millscale. It was then wire-brushed off and paint slapped on. Of course all the tiny pits created could not be cleaned out, and the paint scheme inevitably failed after a few years.

Other methods of steel plate cleaning include acid pickling (immersing in acid solution for a few hours) and flame-cleaning in which an oxy-acetylene flame is passed over the plate to spall away the millscale and rust.

Today blast-cleaning is common practice and gives a very clean finish. For small areas, grinding with hand-held power tools is also possible and given patience and good quality control the surface finish is as good as blastcleaning.

Plates and bars can be bought blast-cleaned and 'shop primed'. The paint is sprayed on immediately after cleaning. However a steel surface is cleaned, it is absolutely essential to apply the paint as soon as possible. Even in dry and warm conditions a few *hours* may be too long and the surface can become damp and dusty again. The 'shop primer', 'blast primer' or 'pre-treatment primer' is a quick-drying paint that will give protection for a number of months and

173

will not affect any subsequent cutting or welding process. It is also a suitable base for the main paint scheme. Thus when the hull is completed it can be painted directly. Areas where the shop primer has been burned or ground off can be either shot-blasted *in situ* or, more practically, be ground flush and clean with a power grinder and then immediately shop primed.

Alternatively, bare steel can be purchased, fabricated into a hull and then blast-cleaned, but the problem here is that pitting will already have commenced and it will be difficult to blast clean the interior (if not impossible in places).

Blast-Cleaning

This technique involves throwing small abrasive particles against the steel surface by either rotating impellers or compressed air. In both cases the grit can be recycled, so metallic grit – steel or cast iron grit, or steel shot of about 1 mm diameter – is used. Without recycling a cheap and expendable abrasive must be used; it is made from slag or mineral matter. Sand used to be used until it was found that it was a danger to health; for industrial use, in many countries sand is barred. Blast-cleaning is a noisy, messy and tedious business, hence the attraction of pre-blasted and shop primed plates.

Blast-cleaning steel is generally done to Second Quality Finish of BS 4232 which is equivalent to 'Near White' of the American SSPC standard and SA $2\frac{1}{2}$ of the Swedish Standards Commission. It is important that this level of cleanliness is achieved otherwise the subsequent paint scheme will fail prematurely.

These standards specify the cleanliness and roughness of the blast-cleaned surface. At least 95% of the surface should be bare and clean, the remainder being tightly adherent residues of mill-scale and rust in very small and defined patches. First Quality (or 'White', or SA3) involves cleaning 100% of the surface. Third Quality ('Commercial', or SA2) is intended for steel that is to be painted with conventional paint for exposure to mild corrosive atmospheres.

Apart from new-building, blast-cleaning can be applied to an old steel hull in order to build a good paint scheme. The outside can be done fairly simply but interiors are usually impractical. In any case adjacent boats are likely to become covered in dust and grit, so the complete repainting of a steel boat hull can be an onerous or expensive task.

A 'high performance' paint scheme on a blast-cleaned hull will last several years at least, and ten years can be expected especially if the boat is ashore and covered up each winter. Indeed in this case twenty years can pass before a complete strip and repaint is necessary. Of course 'repainting' in the sense of adding a single top coat is necessary every two years or so for the sake of a glossy appearance. This practice has also been shown to increase the life of the original coats.

Paints

Having arranged a clean dry surface, what type of paint should be used? There are basically two broad types: the 'conventional' types of paint, either oil-based or using natural or synthetic resin (oleo-resinous, bitumen, alkyd, phenolic, and coal tar), and the newer high performance types (epoxide, polyurethane, chlorinated rubber, vinyl, zinc silicate, and coal tar epoxide). For a steel boat it is usually far better to choose a high performance paint inside and out – and probably more economical in the long run, at least for those on salt waters. High performance paints are much more expensive than conventional ones but nevertheless most steel hulls built today (ships and boats) are epoxide or polyurethane painted. However, the high performance paints are more sensitive to good surface cleanliness and to the atmospheric conditions at the time of painting. Indeed, if wire-brushing is all that can be done by way of preparation then high performance paints are a waste of money.

When choosing paints, select a reputable manufacturer and follow his recommendations. That way all the necessarily different coatings will be compatible with each other, and providing surface preparation and atmospheric conditions are right, success will be probable. Paint manufacturers publish excellent free informative literature and do seem to be very willing to give advice on particular problems. The boat owner can do no better than to lean on this advice.

CONTROL AND PREVENTION

The following is an example by International Paints Ltd. for an epoxy based scheme.

Bottoms – High Build Epoxy – Airless spray application directly after blast cleaning.

Product name	Film thickness		Sequential overcoating intervals	
	WFT	DFT	15°C	23°C
Intergard Primer Red	85μ	40μ	**min** 16 hrs **max** 6 mths	12 hrs 6 mths
Interprime 820 Grey	216μ	125μ	**min** 16 hrs **max** 6 mths	6 hrs 6 mths
Interprime 820 White	216μ	125μ	**min** 16 hrs **max** 6 mths	6 hrs 6 mths
Interprotect Grey	305μ	125μ	**min** 5 hrs **max** 3 days	3 hrs 2 days
International Antifouling (x2 coats)	See appropriate Data Sheet for details.			

Topsides Deck and Deckhouse Airless primers/conventional spray finishes

As per bottoms but with polyurethane instead of the Interprotect tie coat and antifouling. When fairing is required Interfill 830 and 833 should be applied in thicknesses up to 10mm after the Interguard primer.

Polyurethane Basecoat	100μ	50μ	**min** 16 hrs **max** 3 days	10 hrs 2 days
Interspray 900 (x2 coats) Plus	75μ	37μ	**min** 14 hrs **max** 3 days	6 hrs 2 days
Interspray 900 **Glaze Coat** mixed 50:50 with colour	75μ	37μ	**min** 14 hrs **max** 3 days	6 hrs 2 days
Interspray 900 (x2 coats) Plus non slip additive for decks	75μ	37μ	**min** 14 hrs **max** 3 days	6 hrs 2 days

176

Maintenance Painting

Above water   Where the condition of the old paint is sound and adherent, simply wash it down and dry and apply one or two new coats. Where there is slight rusting and blistering, wire-brush thoroughly, wash and dry, and then apply one coat of inhibitive primer and one or two top coats. For badly rusted surfaces blast-clean and renew the paint scheme entirely.

Underwater   Where there is negligible rusting remove slime and fouling and re-antifoul. Where some rusting has occuured remove slime and fouling and scale back locally to sound paint. Touch-up with the original anticorrosion paint. Coat with one or two coats of anticorrosive paint and one or two coats of antifouling. On bad rusting blast-clean and apply an entirely new paint scheme.

Special Areas

Deck plating: suggested alternative schemes.

> Zinc-spray 50 μm + aluminium spray 125 μm + one coat zinc chrome primer + one coat non-slip deck paint 60 μm.
>
> Two coats red lead + two coats chlorinated rubber 130 μm.
>
> One coat epoxide primer + epoxide resin 600 μm.

Steel drinking water tanks: suggested schemes.

> Two coats bitumen solution + one coat bitumen enamel to BS 3416 Type (to avoid water taint) 125 μm.
>
> Coal tar enamel to BS 4164 Appendix Q (to avoid water taint).

General principles

The paint scheme chosen can vary according to the 'aggressiveness' of the environment: for instance one of the worst areas is the lower part of the hull just above the waterline, which is alternately wetted and dried. The cabin roof will be washed with rain and most of the time will be clean and free of salt, since a pleasure boat is moored idle most of the time. The outside of the bottom is not a great problem area because there conditions are constant and maintenance easy, compared to the internal bilges for instance or built-in tanks where rusting is so often a problem. Just as important as the choice of paint and the preparation of the steel is easy access to the inside of the bilges in order to repaint. Also good continuous drainage of condensation down to the lowest bilge is vital in order to avoid water traps. Similarly, free ventilation of the bilges is important.

This is digression: the point is, different areas may require different treatments. However, for the sake of simplicity many boatbuilders use epoxide throughout on shop-primed plate. Where welding has been done and the primer burned off, a power tool is used to grind and buff smooth the damaged strips, which are then primed. Modern practice is to build all-welded hulls of mild steel that has been shop primed at the mill, and after completion to coat with epoxide up to the thickness recommended by the paint manufacturer. A polyurethane coat might be used where a good gloss is required. (Epoxide tends to go chalky after some time.) A good builder will give the welded areas an extra stripe coat of primer, knowing that rust will always break out first at joins, corners or attachments.

Old fashioned red lead should never be used below the waterline because it goes soft. It is satisfactory well above the waterline when overcoated with conventional paints. This remark also applies to all oil-based, alkyd, and oleo-resinous paints, which means that only coal tar, phenolic or bitumen conventional paints should be used underwater.

Coal tar epoxide (a mixture of epoxide and coal tar) is cheaper than pure epoxide but harder wearing and apparently just as effective. It is very popular for ships' bottoms. Like epoxy it goes on very thickly and two coats are usually sufficient. It tends to bleed through a light coloured top coat (or even antifouling) but this can be prevented by a barrier coat.

The other high performance paints are less commonly used in steel boatbuilding. Chlorinated rubber can be painted on at very low temperatures and is a 'thick' leathery paint which has been proved to be as good as epoxide. Vinyl is a 'thinner' paint and is also difficult to apply by brush; it needs good weather conditions, but properly applied performs as well as epoxide.

Interior

The bilges and interior of a steel hull ought also to have a high performance paint scheme because all too often it is the interior that causes corrosion problems rather than the exterior. This is especially true in the case of built-in fresh water or fuel tanks. It is attractive to simply build a welded box on the bottom of the boat, but in my opinion it is far better to fit separate tanks of perhaps a different and more corrosion resistant material. Built-in tanks ought at least to have an amply sized access hatch in their tops, so that they can be cleaned and (epoxide) painted inside. A white colour makes cleaning easier.

Fresh Water Craft

Corrosion in fresh water is far less and conventional paints can last a reasonable length of time. On narrow and shallow canals like the canals of Britain with locks only a few inches wider than the boat, bumps and grazes are inevitable and even the toughest high performance paint will get knocked off. So the policy of using a cheap black varnish slapped on regularly is sensible, at least for the sides and bottom; but for the deck and interior of the hull it is worth considering a high performance paint.

Colour

Dark colours absorb the sun's heat more than light colours or white. On a steel boat it is a positive advantage to have the temperature of the above-water steelwork a few degrees above the air temperature. This ensures that internal condensation and external dew are driven off. So darker colours are preferable for a steel boat. (Of course this makes the interior of the cabin hotter in a hot climate, but heat insulation ought to be fitted in any metal boat.)

Interestingly, this is in direct contrast to a wooden hull where the sun's heat tends to dry out the timber and crack the paint so that light colours are preferable on a wooden hull.

Zinc-Rich Paints

One particular type of zinc-rich paint is designed to create cathodic protection of the underlying steel. The paint contains so much zinc – no less than 92% –that it can conduct electricity. Other zinc-rich paints have a lesser quantity of zinc but nevertheless appear to give good protection. In this class are zinc-silicates, which have very good abrasion resistance and non-slip properties: hence they are good for decks. Zinc-rich paints are not yet reliable underwater.

Zinc-rich paints are sometimes referred to as 'cold galvanizing' but the protection given is nowhere near as much as hot-dip galvanizing. One area where they are useful is for touching up damaged areas of hot-dip galvanizing.

Paint Thickness Measurement

Since paint film thickness is an important factor to the life of the coating some approximate means of measuring the dry thickness is desirable. Instruments are made that measure the dry film thickness directly, using magnetic principles; they do not damage the paint. Failing that, a rough idea can be gained from the amount of paint used. Knowing this and the area over which it was applied one can work out the thickness. But there are allowances to be made: splash may lose 10% of the paint (20% if it is sprayed on). A rough surface may lose an additional 20% as calculated from plane area; a smooth surface will lose 5%. Then there is the reduction in thickness as the paint dries. Coal tar epoxide reduces to 80%, an aluminium bitumen paint to 45%. Any answer derived by the calculation is bound to be very vague, it is better to ask the manufacturer for the direct conversion factor of spreading rate to dry film thickness.

Rust Raisers

If one looks at a steel boat that is 'middle-aged' it becomes clear that rust always starts first at discontinuities – edges, bolt or rivet heads, stanchion ' bases, weld beads, etc. Smooth uninterrupted plates remain rust-free for a very long time. Areas of chafe are also 'rust raisers', such as on bollards, or where ropes run or anchor chains rub.

Thus to specify 'shot-blasting and epoxide coating' is not the complete answer to the rust problem. Detail design is most important, in order to avoid water traps, sharp corners and inaccessible areas. Intermittent welding on the exterior of the hull should not be allowed because any steel items in close contact – but not actually welded together – will be inacessible to paint and

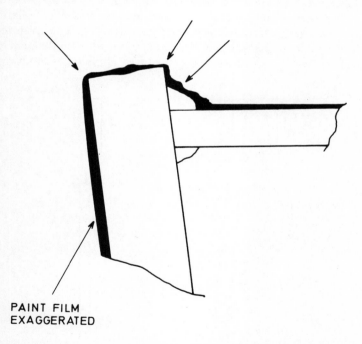

PAINT FILM
EXAGGERATED

(31) Paint films are by no means constant in thickness: the paint drains away from sharp corners and the spikes of roughness. Rusting always starts first at these points. Water traps should also be avoided.

rusting will very soon start. Weld beads should ideally be ground smooth. The gunwale should not trap water, and the exposed edges of all plating should be ground smooth and their sharp corners rounded off.

The fewer the number of items attached to the deck and superstructure the better, remembering that smooth continuous areas of plate will not rust. The best steel boats look 'clean' and uncluttered, though of course certain items have to be fitted. Stanchions should be set clear enough from the toerail or other obstructions so that drainage, cleaning and repainting around their bases is easy. All items bolted to the deck ought to be set in a bedding compound. Galvanized bolts should be used or, even better, stainless steel, so that subsequent removal of the item is easy.

Areas subject to chafe or wear can be made of stainless steel or be galvanized or zinc-sprayed. For instance stainless steel bollards can be welded direct to the deck; mild steel cleats can be galvanized before welding in place. Other items that come to mind that can be galvanized or made of stainless steel are chainplates, bulwark

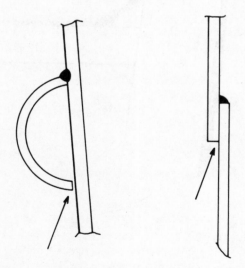

(32) All crevices and void spaces should be sealed, preferably by welding or by a sealing compound, otherwise rust stains will forever be a problem.

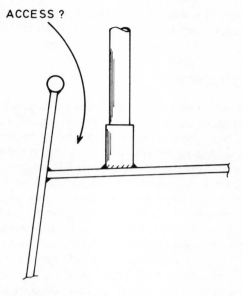

ACCESS ?

(33) Always allow access for painting.

capping tubes and rubbing stakes, rubbing plates for anchor chain and mooring lines.

Decks which take heavy wear can be zinc-sprayed and painted. Wood sheathing on a steel deck can cause very rapid rusting: water becomes trapped underneath and of course the steel cannot be regularly painted. A palliative measure is to prime the steel and then put on a thick layer of bitumen bedding compound before laying the (caulked) planking or plywood, which should be rot-proofed. A sheet of polythene between the steel and the wood is another trick.

The philosophy of a 'clean' structure and careful detail design applies equally to the hull interior. Drainage is particularly important. Limber holes in longitudinal stiffeners should have a clear hole of 1 in. (25 mm) at least, so that condensation cannot collect but will run down to the keel. Frameless construction is attractive from the bilge corrosion point of view; cleaning and repainting are also made easier. Ventilation of the bilge and behind linings is important to dry out condensation. Heat insulation should be glued direct to the steelwork after painting so that there is no air gap between it and the shell. The insulation ought also to be vapour sealed with polythene sheet.

Galvanic precautions

Like aluminium, steel is low down in the galvanic series, so one has to beware of attaching items which are more noble (as described in Chapter 7). Brass or bronze sterngear (the propeller shaft, stern-tube, etc) ought to be electrically isolated from the hull as should bronze skin fittings, etc. Actually, even if they are not, corrosion will not be on a massive scale but localized and slow. This is especially the case if highly insulating epoxide paints are used and if the *noble* items are well coated. Zinc anodes are well worth fitting in any case to aid the paint scheme and to stop corrosion at breaks in the paint film. Zinc anodes will stop the galvanic effects of electrically coupled sterngear. (Consult the specialists for the number, type and positions for these anodes.)

Specifying two coats of coal tar epoxide over a blast-cleaned bottom plus zinc anodes will mean a trouble-free outer bottom for many years: certainly the underwater area will cause far less trouble than other high-risk areas such as the bilges and tanks.

An aluminium deckhouse needs careful isolation (see Chapter 7). Cast iron keels of course present no problem on the steel hull, but a lead keel needs insulation as will the bronze bolts where they come through the steel bottom.

Molten lead can be conveniently poured direct into a steel keel, thus dispensing with a mould. By cleaning the steel first and using a flux it ought to be possible to create a bond so that water cannot get between the lead and the steel to cause corrosion. Otherwise the top of the lead and the adjacent steelwork should be given a thick coating of bitumen compound which is run down into any crevices between the lead and the steel plating.

A two-wire electrical system (rather than earth return) should be used to avoid electrolytic action. Mooring alongside a copper sheathed boat for long periods should also be avoided.

Metal Coated Steel Hulls

A galvanized and painted steel surface is very enduring and rust-free; so is zinc or aluminium sprayed (and painted) steel. It is therefore attractive to consider a hull treated thus. Certainly galvanized or sprayed hulls are far less common than plain steel ones, but this is probably because boatbuilders are not so familiar with the process.

Before ships' lifeboats were made of fibreglass they were often made of rivetted galvanized plate and these did last a long time. Dutch boatbuilders sometimes zinc-spray their steel hulls, and steel boats are very common in Holland.

Plates can be bought already galvanized (but make sure the galvanizing is to a good thickness). Fabricated by welding into a hull, the zinc coating is burned off local to the weld, but this area can be repaired afterwards by shot-blasting and zinc-spraying. Actually, good results are achieved in this application, with zinc-rich paint, providing the paint is applied to clean, ground-off steel. Galvanizing does not affect the strength of the weld but it does cause dense fumes which over a sufficient time can give the welder 'zinc fever'. Welders therefore do not like the work; however an air suction line can overcome the problem.

Zinc or aluminium spraying after completion is another alternative. The problem is that the areas to be sprayed must first be blast-cleaned, which inside a completed hull is not so easy. Again frameless construction helps matters, and it is not nearly so difficult on a *bare* hull shell compared to one which has been fully fitted out. Not all the hull need be sprayed, of course; only those areas prone to rust such as the lower bilge inside, the decks, and along joints (e.g. coaming to deck). The outer hull topsides and bottom also benefit, but these 'clean' uninterrupted surfaces are usually the least troublesome.

Zinc or aluminium are equally good as far as protection is concerned, the main requirement being a blast-cleaned surface. A combination coat is apparently even better: zinc 50 μm thick and then aluminium 125 μm. This is the practice of some navies for weather decks. Whatever the system, a sprayed coating should be at least 100 μm (4 mils) or to a standard, e.g. BS 2569 Part 1 as described in Chapter 4.

In the spraying process molten metal is sprayed onto the steel and it adheres and cools very quickly. It forms an excellent tough and clean surface for subsequent painting. The thickness is very much determined by the operator's skill and at least two passes with the spray nozzle should be made to ensure no thin areas. Zinc or aluminium of high purity should be used. (In the UK this is covered in BS 3436 which specifies 99.9% zinc, and BS 1475 with 99.5% aluminium).

Since both blast-cleaning and metal spraying require a powerful compressor and should be done consecutively within an hour or so of each other, it pays to get the same contractor to do both jobs.

Both galvanizing and zinc or aluminium spraying give a very tough rust-free finish. Even if the coating is scratched ugly rust streaks do not appear because of the galvanic protection given by the metal. This is a drawback of a paint-only scheme: whenever the paint gets damaged rusting inevitably starts immediately.

Painting Metal Coatings

Adhesion of paint to a hot-dip galvanized surface is a problem if some basic rules are not observed. A hot-dip galvanized surface is too smooth for the paint to get a 'grip' and it is usually contaminated by flux or grease. Also the zinc is active and tends to react chemically with many paints (e.g. alkyds), spoiling the adhesion after a time. The first problem can be countered by roughening the surface, the second by de-greasing, and the third by using an etch primer or pre-treatment primer.

Thus the painting procedure should be: degrease with white spirit, apply one coat of pre-treatment primer which roughens and neutralizes the surface, and then put on the paint scheme which can be a high performance paint ideally or a conventional paint.

Weathering the surface rather than using an etch primer is an old method which does not give such good results.

Of the sprayed coatings, aluminium has been found to be less reactive than zinc and need not therefore have an etch primer. Weathering of either is deleterious. A zinc-sprayed coating should be etch primed. Conventional or high performance paint schemes can then be used.

Aluminium Hulls

Rust is the major problem with a steel boat and galvanic corrosion *can* be the bugbear of an aluminium boat. But galvanic troubles can be avoided, whereas rust is virtually inevitable. Aluminium craft made of marine grade aluminium and designed and built with galvanic effects kept in mind (as described in Chapter 7) have proved to be very trouble-free and long lasting. In the UK remnants of suspicion still remain regarding the corrosion behaviour of aluminium boats in seawater. (The early use of aluminium before the Second World War using the wrong alloys and without too much regard for galvanic questions led to many failures.) In America in particular, aluminium boats are common, from small rivetted canoes to large offshore patrol boats.

A 20–30 ft (6–9 m) welded aluminium hull is about a third of the weight of a steel one since the thicknesses used are comparable, and such a hull is usually a little lighter than a fibreglass or a traditionally built wooden one. The other attraction of aluminium is its corrosion resistance since marine grade corrodes at a very low rate in or above seawater. The surface goes 'spotty' and gritty to the touch, but need only be painted if a colour is required. The correct procedure for painting aluminium is similar to that for galvanized steel: degreasing, etch primer, and a paint scheme that may be conventional or high performance. The interior out-of-sight parts of the hull need not be painted at all. Paints containing lead, copper or mercury should be avoided like the plague.

Wood decks on top of aluminium should also be avoided because of the danger of poultice corrosion.

Galvanic precautions in practice mean electrically insulating any metal fitting which is made of a metal above aluminium in the galvanic series (see Chapter 7). Keels and keel bolts, propellers, shafts, rudders and seacocks ought to be insulated. Propellers, rudders, sterntubes and seacocks can be made of aluminium (thus dispensing with insulation), and this is a sensible approach rather than choosing bronze for instance. Bronze in particular, and brass, are killers to an aluminium hull if the electrical insulation is not sound. Any underwater item more noble than aluminium should be painted with a thick, preferably epoxy, coating even if the rest of the hull is bare.

Above water and on deck electrical insulation must still be carried out; the only metals that in some cases need not be insulated are stainless steel, Monel and galvanized steel.

Engine cooling pipes should be connected to the seacocks with a short length of plastic or rubber hose; indeed the whole engine installation should be insulated from the hull. This is not too difficult with such commonly used items as water-lubricated rubber shaft bearings, rubber exhaust hose and rubber engine mountings. A two-wire electrical system should be fitted.

Fuel and water tanks can quite happily be formed as part of the hull and left unpainted, but large removable panels should be put in the top so that cleaning can be carried out every few years.

An owner of an aluminium boat is wise to ensure that there is no electrically conducting path between his hull and a steel jetty or marina pontoon, nor to a copper-sheathed boat alongside. With plastic fenders and synthetic fibre warps this insulation is usually taken care of.

Aluminium has poorer fatigue properties compared to steel and fatigue cracking is more likely. This can occasionally happen in the plating above the propellers or in the chainplates or engine bearers due to engine vibration. However this problem is usually not at all serious on small craft.

Welded or Rivetted?

The choice depends on which aluminium alloy is chosen – heat-treatable or non-heat-treatable – and on the thickness. Plate of less than about $\frac{1}{8}$ in. (3 mm) thickness is not easily welded and also distortion becomes a problem. The heat-treatable alloys are strengthened by heat-treatment, as their name suggests. If such an alloy is welded the process locally reduces its strength back to that of the non-heat-treatable alloys. Consequently welded hulls use $\frac{1}{8}$ in. to $\frac{1}{4}$ in. (3–6 mm) thick plates of a non-heat-treatable alloy. Smaller hulls (canoes, dinghies etc) which require thinner plate are therefore mostly rivetted using the stronger heat-treatable alloy.

Where joints are rivetted it is vital to keep out the water otherwise sticky white jelly will forever ooze out: the result of corrosion in the mating surfaces. Just prior to rivetting, the mating surfaces should be treated with a flexible sealant; PRC is often used and the joint rivetted up wet. The principle of avoiding crevices where water could lie (or sealing those crevices) is an important part of building an aluminium boat, almost as important as avoiding galvanic conditions. (PRC sealants are marketed by Products Research & Chemical Corp. in Los Angeles and Berger Paints in the UK.) Sikaflex is another much used product.

Copper Sheathing and Copper-Nickel Hulls

A chapter on metal hulls would be incomplete without reference to the old-time practice of copper sheathing and the exciting possibilities of copper-nickel hulls (albeit only a reality for a rich few).

Copper sheathing became common practice on many sailing ships following experiments on HMS *Alarm* in 1763. The main object of this experiment had been to prevent worms reaching the hull timbers, but it was soon proved that the copper for some reason stopped weed and barnacles from becoming attached. Consequently the ships did not suffer the serious speed loss which heavy fouling always caused.

Some metals form a toxic surface film when immersed in seawater: a film which is poisonous to animal life. These metals or their alloys include chromium, copper, zinc, silver, mercury and tin. Zinc, in more recent tests, remained antifouling for two years after which it fouled rapidly in seawater. But copper is the best antifouler and it remained common practice to copper sheath wooden boats right up until the advent of fibreglass. This was especially so if the boat was intended for tropical waters, where the rate of fouling and the worm population are far higher than in colder climates. The copper sheets overlapped and were fastened with copper boat nails.

The ability of copper to resist fouling stems from its corrosion product cuprous oxide, not because poisonous copper ions are released into the water. Consequently copper will not protect an adjacent surface; fouling will occur right up to the edge where the copper begins. Also, because the copper must corrode slightly in

189

order to form a toxic film any galvanic protection of the copper's surface will inhibit its antifouling property. For instance, on a copper sheathed boat a sacrificial anode system or even the presence of an underwater fitting of less noble metal such as steel will cause the copper to foul. In the report to the Admiralty in 1763 it was mentioned that 'The copper which was remaining on the bottom had been on near Twenty Months and had kept perfectly clean without any means having been used to render it so. But the Copper which covered the Rother [made of iron] was foul'd with Barnacles; and this difference we cannot Account for unless it may be supposed, that the Plates there being fastened with IRON NAILS which was done to vary the experiment . . .'.

The gentlemen writing this report concluded first that the copper plate stopped the worm and prevented fouling, and second that iron must not be used anywhere in conjunction with the sheathing, partly for galvanic reasons and partly because the antifouling property is impaired: conclusions that are still valid today.

A copper sheathed boat must therefore have all underwater fasteners and fittings of a metal at least as noble as copper.

Copper-Nickel Hulls

The idea of a non-corroding, non-fouling metal hull (solid as opposed to sheathed) is very attractive and the idea has been tried many times. Around the beginning of the century wealthy yachting gentlemen had large yachts built of brass and Monel. One in particular was built of a mixture of Monel and steel. Of course it was a disaster, and the vessel was soon scrapped!

The copper content of an alloy has to be high in order for it to have an antifouling effect. Both Monel and brass do not have a high enough content, but copper-nickel does. In fact, in static tests samples of copper and 90/10 and 70/30 copper-nickel showed much the same fouling resistance over a five year period. The plates were fouled at the end of this time but far less than in the case of steel and aluminium plates, which were thick with encrustation within a year. (The tests were carried out in an area which is classed 'moderate to heavily fouling'). In any case the fouling on copper and copper-nickel is easily washed off, unlike that on aluminium for instance. Indeed if the boat puts to sea regularly her hull remains virtually clean. This fact has been proved in practice with several copper-nickel shrimp fishing boats operating in highly fouling warm Central American waters. These vessels have operated alongside similar steel ones and whereas the steel ones have to be cleaned and antifouled every six months the copper-nickel hulls have not yet been cleaned (they were built in 1973).

Apart from its antifouling property copper-nickel is virtually non-corrodible in seawater. It is easily formed and welded for construction. Indeed it can be welded quite easily to mild steel, using 70/30 copper-nickel or Monel welding rods. Thus it is only necessary to plate the underwater hull with the expensive material; the internal framing and upperworks can, if need be, be made of cheap mild steel. It is reasonably strong (ample at least for small boats) and has good fatigue properties and no nasty corrosion habits.

Apart from the shrimpers, several yachts have been made of copper-nickel (usually 90/10) and if one has the money it is clearly the best of all hull materials. Note that all underwater items should then be made of the same material or a more noble metal: a vital point.

A future possibility along these lines is the sheathing during manufacture of the bottoms of fibreglass hulls with 90/10 copper-nickel. If some means could be found of bonding paper-thin copper-nickel plates to a curved fibreglass hull the antifouling yacht paint manufacturers would be put out of business! Copper-nickel is stronger than copper and its corrosion rate is far less, both factors making it possible to use very thin sheets for sheathing and thus to keep the cost down.

Other exotic materials which have been suggested for hull construction include titanium and stainless steel. Neither would be antifouling but stainless steel might be cheaper than copper-nickel. Hulls have been made of stainless steel, but must be guarded against pitting corrosion by painting the bottom and using sacrificial anodes.

Chapter 13
Engine Corrosion

Direct and Indirect Cooling

Two types of engine cooling are commonly employed on water-cooled engines; one involves pumping raw sea or river water straight through the block, the other is a closed circuit system using a heat exchanger where the engine heat is passed to the water outside.

After reading Chapter 4 on Steel and Iron, one realizes that an iron engine block will corrode quite rapidly if seawater is pumped through it. Slow-running true marine engines are made of cast iron just like marinized car or truck engines, so they will corrode just as quickly. However the water passages of true marine engines are made larger to allow for silting up and the thickness of the casting is made greater to give a margin for rusting. Nevertheless a direct-cooled engine can last a long time before the cast iron block corrodes right through; in fact, in most cases the engine has to be scrapped because of some other cause like cylinder corrosion or the consequences of neglect.

There are two ways in which corrosion in the water passages in the engine can be reduced. First, many direct-cooled engines have zinc sacrificial anodes screwed into the block, and it pays to replace these when they are almost corroded away. Second, when the engine is laid up for the winter a thorough cleaning and corrosion inhibiting procedure is advisable.

This entails flushing the system through with clean fresh water and then with a rust-inhibiting solution, commonly done by disconnecting the water intake hose from the seacock and extending it to a large drum of clean water. The engine is then started

Products of corrosion between the aluminium hub and the bronze spline has created enough force to split the hub. Best to keep this type of propeller out of the water (it is an outboard/outdrive propeller).

The effect of a fast stream of water (possibly cavitating) on an aluminium duct – in this case a waterjet intake. The tough epoxide paint coating has long gone. It took some 5000 hours of running over two years to get to this state. The close proximity of a large stainless steel impeller probably also had a lot to do with it. A GRP duct would fare better.

A stainless steel shaft was running inside this aluminium tube which was filled with seawater. The inside was painted, but galvanic action concentrated its effect on the weakest part of the paint film. Perforation of the 10 mm thick wall occurred after only a year. Painting the shaft – the more noble of the two metals – would improve the situation but the paint would get rubbed off the shaft as it was pushed up the bearing. A GRP tube would be a much better solution with anodes to protect the shaft.

A similar situation, but here the inside of the tube was unpainted. The aluminium in this case was 6000 series (an extrusion) rather than the more corrosion resistant 5000 series.

Heavy pitting and almost rust-like flaking on this piece of aluminium plate that lay close to a stainless steel shaft bracket without protection from zinc anodes.

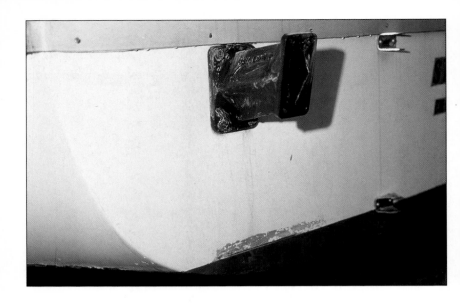

These two photographs show rust bleeding from bolts which are mild steel (possibly bare or more probably zinc electro-plated) fitted in the belief that the plating would last.

Rust bleeding from the interface between the top of the iron keel and the hull. Maybe it is the iron that is corroding away or worse, the keel bolts. A worrying situation only relieved by dropping the keel and investigating.

An aluminium stern tube inside which a stainless shaft had been running for a year. The tube was painted and antifouled but still suffered badly; in one place the 10 mm thickness was perforated.

A rubber D section fender used to lie along this gunwale. Serious attack has taken place not through any nasty chemical seeping out of the rubber, but simply because this is what *may* happen if bare aluminium is placed in close proximity with another surface and water is added. Copious adherent sealant (eg Purflex) is the answer.

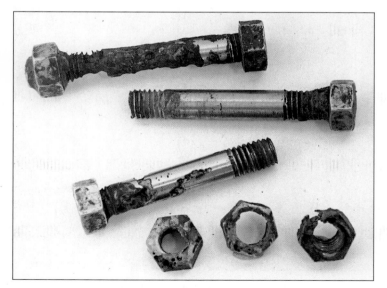

A nice collection of pitted stainless bolts of unknown quality. Type 316 is the best readily available quality. These bolts were probably set in damp wood.

A brass bolt that used to fasten a seacock flange on a wooden boat.
Brass is best avoided on boats except, perhaps, internal joinery work.

Severe pitting of 6000 series aluminium plating in a seawater tank. This can
also happen in freshwater tanks. Use 5000 series aluminium and paint the
inside. Bare aluminium diesel fuel tanks are OK.

A propeller cavitating badly. The bubbles are cavities in the water (not air bubbles) which eventually implode (opposite of explode) and, if this happens on the surface of a metal, it literally plucks bits of metal off. A rudder in the slipstream of a propeller can also be corroded by these cavities, particularly from the hub vortex.

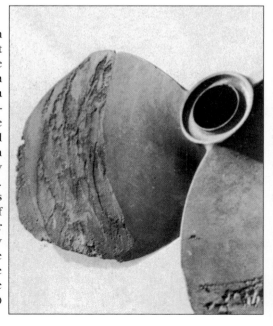

Severe cavitation erosion. For this amount of damage to occur the propeller must have been cavitating very badly, giving a disappointing boat performance. More blade area (ie wider blades) is the usual cure; the diameter and pitch should be reduced only slightly or not at all. Cavitation usually causes pits (as on the blade half out of the picture) rather than a scour, and usually the damage occurs on the forward face of the blade towards the tips or at the root. (Eric Coltham)

and run slowly, topping up the drum of water as necessary. Then a mixture of water and emulsifying inhibiting oil is put in the drum and just as the intake pipe starts to suck air the engine is stopped.

After a few days the engine is drained of the mixture, by which time salts will have had time to dissolve. The internal passageways of the block are then left coated with inhibiting oil. Inhibiting oils are usually not antifreeze agents, hence the need to drain them out.

If a thermostat is fitted, depending on the circuit it may bypass the inhibiting mixture past the block itself, in which case it should be taken out temporarily.

An alternative to inhibiting oil is to use fresh water and an anti-freeze which has an inhibiting oil in it, leaving it in the engine all winter.

Indirect cooling by means of a heat exchanger avoids these problems. The closed circuit system can be left full of fresh water and antifreeze the year round, just like that of a car. The heat exchanger itself is usually made of a copper alloy, for instance inhibited brass or aluminium brass. The velocity of the seawater also has a bearing on material choice, as described in Chapter 6. A heat exchanger system also allows a higher running temperature to be chosen, which is beneficial to engine life and to the noise level.

When laying up, other important parts of the engine to consider are the cylinders. If these rust, the consequences are serious. Inhibiting oil should be put in each cylinder and then the inlet and exhaust manifolds should be hermetically sealed. This can be done by taking off the rubber exhaust hose where it connects to the water injector head and putting a thick plastic bag over the orifice, holding it tightly to the pipe with rubber bands. The inlet manifold can be sealed in a similar way after taking off the air intake. Of course each engine is different and other means may have to be found to seal the 'breathing' of the engine. A rag stuffed up the exhaust is not good enough. There may also be a crankcase breather and a suction from the tappet cover to seal.

With petrol engines it is easy to put a teaspoonful of inhibiting oil through the sparkplug holes and then to turn the engine over a few times to lubricate the bores. But with a diesel, getting the oil in is not so easy. If heater plugs are fitted then these can be removed. Removing the injectors is not such a good idea because on each occasion one is disturbing several high-pressure seals. There is also the risk of getting dirt in the pipes. Injecting oil into the inlet manifold while the engine is running works for a petrol engine, but a diesel will race away and burn the oil.

There is no ready answer to this problem on a diesel if there are no heater plugs. In temperate climates it is not nearly so essential to rust-inhibit the cylinder bores compared to northern colder latitudes or humid tropics.

The diesel's manufacturers may recommend running the engine on a special fuel oil that prevents corrosion of the fuel pump and injectors. In any event it is wise to obtain a handbook for the engine and carry out the layup as recommended.

The exterior of the engine can be coated with a rust-inhibiting oil and an aerosol spray is useful for this. At all times keep salt spray or rainwater off the engine. İt takes only a few minutes with the engine cover lifted when the boat is running on a breezy day for the engine to get covered in salt crystals which will forever be deliquescent and cause rapid rusting – inhibiting oil or not.

Water Piping

The design of the water piping for the raw cooling water to the engine ought to take fatigue and erosion into account. In other words, it ought to have a flexible section close to the engine allowing ample flexibility for engine movement when running, and in the act of stopping because that is when the engine moves most. A short length of rubber or neoprene pipe does this as well as providing an electrical insulation and reducing the transmission of vibration. Soldered joints are taboo because of their poor fatigue properties. Seawater piping is commonly of copper as the water flow is slow enough – or the actual running time in a boat's lifetime short enough – not to cause corrosion/erosion. Hose clips can be bought of either zinc-plated steel or stainless steel and occasionally Monel. The zinc plating is usually very thin and even in quite mildly aggressive atmospheres rust starts fairly soon. In most situations on seagoing boats it is better in the long run to fit stainless steel hose clips.

Seacocks have been discussed in Chapter 10 on Problem Areas Below Water, but seacock strainers deserve a mention. Often made of brass, they dezincify rapidly as they present such a large surface area to the water. They end up like lace and bits can detach themselves and get sucked up into the pump. A strainer made of perforated copper sheet is the answer.

Water pumps suffer abrasion through sand, and erosion from cavitation or simply a fast flow of water. The better pumps are made of resistant materials. Pitting of a stainless steel pump shaft is another possible trouble especially if a 'cheap' stainless steel is used and is not cathodically protected by the pump body. There is not much one can do except complain bitterly and buy another pump – of another make if possible.

Exhausts

Marine exhausts are either 'dry' or 'wet'. A wet exhaust has cooling water injected into it shortly after it leaves the manifold. This is the most common system since it cools the exhaust as well as silences it, and also allows rubber exhaust hose to be used. The latter avoids corrosion and fatigue problems completely, and helps to reduce vibration transmission.

If a metal exhaust pipe is fitted to a petrol engine the pipe should be made of iron, galvanized steel, copper, brass or stainless steel for both wet or dry systems. On a diesel avoid copper or brass because of the corrosive effects of diesel exhaust fumes. Iron, galvanized steel or stainless steel are suitable.

Hot salt water mixed with hot exhaust gases is a very harsh environment and only the highly corrosion resistant and expensive metals can be expected to last a long time. Obviously thin iron and steel pipes will have a short life. Even when the engine is not running, the inside of the pipe will inevitably have water traps and will be wet with condensation; even with 'dry' exhausts since water is produced in the engine's combustion process. Stainless steel has given a mixed performance, probably because of the varied type of stainless used. Type 316 is the best commercial choice, although this has been known to fail in high-powered engine exhausts particularly near the water injection point.

The water injection bend is particularly onerous on the metal because in addition there is the impingement effect (see Chapter 6).

Just exactly how the water is sprayed into the pipe is vitally important to the rate of erosion. This is up to the engine manufacturer because he usually supplies the injection bend.

Two alloys that have been very successful in this application are nickel alloys 825 (Incoloy) and 625 (Inconel). Alloy 625 in particular has very good corrosion fatigue resistance and is therefore suitable for bellows-type expansion joints. Alloy 825 is first choice in the American Boat and Yacht Council's 'Safe Installation of Exhaust Systems for Propulsion and Auxiliary Machinery'.

There is not a great deal the boat owner can do to prolong the life of his exhaust system. Running the engine on fresh water and inhibiting oil when laying up inhibits the exhaust system as well as the engine in the case of a wet exhaust. Drain taps ought to be fitted in the exhaust run in places where water can accumulate (at a swan-neck bend for instance), but they rarely are. Stainless steel, rubber and plastics are becoming more commonly used for silencers, water 'locks' where the engine is fitted well below the waterline, and piping.

Engine installations are covered by standards (mainly for safety) in most countries and recommendations are laid down for exhaust systems, fuel systems etc. In the UK there are standards by Lloyds, and some engine manufacturers publish good installation practices, e.g. Perkins Sabre Ltd. In the USA, the US Coast Guard and ABS rules apply.

Fuel Tanks

Safety against engine fires really does centre around the fuel tank and fuel system, and it is very wise to install to a good standard – especially in a petrol engined boat.

But this book is about corrosion. Fuel tanks often cause corrosion problems. If the inside of the tank corrodes, the corrosion products eventually end up in the fuel lines and hence the engine. This will happen when the boat is in rough water because the sediment normally lying on the bottom of the tank will be stirred up. Also dirt does get into tanks via dirty fuel, the deck filler plate and from dirt in the atmosphere (via the breather pipe), to add to any corrosion products.

Diesels are particularly prone to damage and stoppage through dirt in their fuel. They are usually protected by a paper element filter which can be easily clogged by an overdose of dirt, so another pre-filter (sediment/water trap) should also be fitted between the tank and the paper filter. Obviously a non-corroding fuel tank is very desirable.

The ideal fuel tank material is fire-resistant, tough and non-corroding. Also it should not chemically react with the fuel. The fire question rules out rubber or plastic. Fibreglass is satisfactory providing the type of resin used is resistant to the fuel. Metal tanks meet the fire resistance criteria, but a metal that does not react with the fuel should be chosen. Recommended fuel tank metals are:

Petrol/gasoline	*Diesel oil*
Tinned or leaded steel	Bare steel or steel coated with lead or tin
Stainless steel	Stainless steel
Aluminium	Aluminium
Monel	Monel
Copper, preferably tinned	
Copper-nickel	Copper-nickel
Brass, preferably tinned	

Copper, brass and galvanized steel react with diesel fuel. Also, some authorities do not recommend brass or copper tanks for petrol because of a slight reaction resulting in gumming-up of the petrol after a long time. Tinned brass or tinned copper are safer. Similarly galvanized steel is suspect for petrol and also for diesel.

Aluminium has a relatively low melting point. With such a tank it is important not to screw a brass inlet or outlet fitting directly into the aluminium because of galvanic corrosion.

An all-welded tank is preferable to a rivetted one on the grounds of crevice corrosion and fuel-tightness.

Tinned or leaded steel is sometimes called Terne plate. It is not ideal for fuel tanks, especially for a seagoing boat, because the tin or lead is more noble than steel and any 'holidays' in the coating will be attacked in a salty environment with the possibility, eventually, of a hole and leakage. For this reason Terne plate is not allowed by the U.S. Coast Guard regulations.

Although bare steel is inhibited to some extent by the diesel fuel, rusting inevitably takes place especially when water inevitably finds its way into the tank via the fuel, a leaky deck filler plate or from internal condensation.

A bare steel tank is perhaps the cheapest but not the best. Certainly it ought to have a large access plate for periodic internal cleaning, and the access plate should itself be readily accessible. Indeed in my opinion this recommendation should apply even to non-corrodable tanks because of the inevitable accumulation of dirt. But some authorities do not recommend access plates because of the risk of leakage.

Stainless steel is perhaps the best material – in welded form. The only question mark is the possibility of pitting corrosion where accumulated pockets of water might lie. This can be obviated by smooth welds, by rounding the bottom corners of the tank, and by dishing the bottom so that any water drains to a sump from which it can be drawn off.

When laying up a boat the vent pipes of the fuel tanks should be blocked up to avoid condensation inside. For the same reason it is best to fill a diesel fuel tank almost full; this also means that you buy the fuel at this year's prices rather than next year's. With petrol this is not such a good idea, for safety reasons and because petrol does go 'stale' and can gum up, although this usually takes longer than six months.

Fuel lines should be of metal, certainly not plastic, and should be either seamless annealed copper, copper-nickel or stainless steel, or aluminium alloy on an aluminium boat. Plain steel tubing is satisfactory for diesel fuel on fresh-water boats. Solder must not be used, partly because of its low melting point (in case of a fire) and partly because of the low fatigue strength.

Water Tanks

There are far fewer problems with water storage tanks. Rubber tanks are good except that cleaning inside them is difficult. Stainless steel, fibreglass (it can taint the water), copper, galvanized steel are all good materials. Steel tanks built into the bottom of a steel hull should be painted (as recommended in the section on steel hulls in Chapter 12) and an access plate provided.

Electrical Items

A salty atmosphere is a harsh environment for an electrical system. Clearly any ferrous material must be avoided in switches, fuse-boxes, light fittings, etc. *Copper* cable must be used with an insulation covering resistant to oil and seawater; PVC is usually recommended. Electrical cable ought to be kept clear of heat (exhausts and stoves), water (bilges), and areas where feet can scuff and kick. It also ought not to run *underneath* any part of the fuel system.

Marine-type switches and fittings, whether designed to be water-tight or not, ought not to have any ferrous content and the easiest way to check this is with a magnet. Watertight fittings must be used in the cockpit and on deck or aloft; deck plugs and sockets, switches, navigation lights, horns etc. These are readily available from chandlers. In sheltered areas (inside an open wheelhouse for instance) or in the cabin, salt mist is still a problem because it permeates everywhere, and even with brass and copper fittings green corrosion products can cause loss of electrical continuity, in switches particularly.

Bimetallic joints with a film of salty damp between them will corrode galvanically with loss of electrical continuity. It is best to solder the joints, 'tin' the two surfaces, or use the same metals. In the case of a copper wire going to a steel item such as the engine block, the wire terminal should be tinned.

Battery terminals are often a continual source of interrupted continuity. The battery acid causes voluminous corrosion products to form on the lead terminals and the brass connecting lugs (which ought to be tinned). The oft-recommended cure is to smear petroleum based jelly (Vaseline) all over the connections.

Instruments (temperature gauge, et al) intended for cars do not last very well on a seagoing boat: they are usually not waterproof nor free of ferrous parts. Even with marine type instruments it is not wise to put them in a position where they will be sprayed with seawater.

A two-wire electrical system rather than 'earth return' should always be fitted, with attention to insulation from underwater metal fittings or sterngear on the hull in order to avoid stray currents and electrolytic problems. The metallic path from the battery to these underwater fittings can be very devious indeed, as mentioned in Chapter 8. A battery master switch, switched off when the boat is left idle, is a good insurance against electrolytic corrosion and also against finding a discharged battery after a week or so.

Outboard Motors

There are a number of useful tips to know about on the subject of outboards and corrosion, and most apply also to sterndrive (inboard – outboard) units.

For instance, never tilt the leg higher than the horizontal if the motor has just come off the water. When lifting it, or in putting it into a car, it is all too easy to get the propeller at a higher level than the head, causing water in the exhaust to run down into the cylinders via the exhaust ports. A motor left like this will seize solid after a time if the water is seawater.

Do not paint the leg with an antifouling containing copper or mercury, nor fix anything to it that is not of stainless or galvanized steel.

If the motor is to be laid up give it a good flush through with fresh water. This should prevent the chance of nasty hydroxide corrosion products oozing out of crevices in the water passages. Flushing through is best done by running the motor in a tub of clean water because then inhibiting oil can be dripped or sprayed into the air intake at the same time. Also, when laying up wash off the outside of the motor with fresh water to get rid of salt crystals which if left will keep the surface damp and highly corrosive.

When the boat is idle it is wise to leave the motor tilted up so that most of the leg is above water. This reduces the chance of contamination of the gear oil, avoids weed and slime growth on the leg, and also prevents galvanic or electrolytic action.

Do not cover the head with a plastic bag because condensation will then form inside on cold days and when the sun comes out the motor will cook inside its 'greenhouse'. Use a canvas cover with air gaps around the underside.

Change the gear oil at the intervals recommended by the engine maker and use the correct oil. The oil inhibits corrosion if seawater does get in the gearcase. Some leakage of water is inevitable through the propeller shaft seals so regular oil changes keep the water content low.

Keep control linkages and the mounting clamp threads well greased.

If an outboard motor is accidentally dropped in the water and then retrieved, it is essential to take action fairly soon – a matter of hours rather than days – because if seawater enters the cylinders and crankcase it will play havoc with the bearing surfaces. The best thing to do is to get the motor running again straight away if possible. Leaving it for the dealer on Monday morning will be too late. If the motor will not start, even after drying out the electrics and flushing water out of the tank and carburetter, then some manufacturers recommend that it be re-submerged in fresh water to avoid exposure to the air. An alternative is to fill the crankcase and cylinder with oil after spinning the motor over to get rid of as much water as possible. Then take it to a service agent.

Chapter 14
Seawater, Sea Salt and
Corrosion Preventers

Pure water is surprisingly non-corrosive. But as soon as impurities are present water becomes to some degree a conductor of electricity so that galvanic cells can be set up which in turn cause corrosion.

Seawater in the oceans and open seas has a high salt content of about 3.5% which does not vary very much around the world except at the mouths of fresh water rivers or in very hot enclosed seas. The 'salt' in seawater is sodium chloride (table salt) and it is this that makes seawater such a good conductor of electricity – and therefore so much more corrosive than fresh water.

The corrosive nature of water is very much related to its conductivity, or in the opposite sense to its resistivity. The resistivity of various 'waters' varies greatly, as shown here.

Ohms per cubic centimetre	
Pure water	20,000,000
Distilled	500,000
Rain	20,000
Tap	5,000
River	200
Coastal	30
Deep seawater	20–25

Calcium carbonate and magnesium sulphate are also present in seawater in small quantities and tend to form a hard white coating over materials immersed in quiet seawater. This happens particularly if a metal surface is cathodically protected, and the scale so formed (after a few months) is protective. Bare steel (e.g. a scratch on a steel hull) which is cathodically protected quickly becomes coated.

Oxygen is also present dissolved in seawater. Most corrosion can only take place when oxygen is present and therefore the level of dissolved oxygen is important. In the open sea there is about 4–8 parts per million, ample to allow steel to corrode. The level drops in stagnant or oil covered waters (canals, bilges) and also in polluted waters. Whereas a low level of oxygen inhibits the corrosion of steel it increases the tendency of stainless steel (and those metals relying on tight adherent oxide films) to pit.

In polluted waters some types of bacteria can create conditions ripe for corrosion at an accelerated rate, often in the form of pitting. The smell of rotten eggs is a sure sign that these bacteria are present. Most metals succumb to badly polluted waters, particularly steel and copper alloys and even Monel.

The acidity or alkalinity of the water also plays a part. Seawater is slightly alkaline with a pH value of about 8.2 (a neutral solution has a pH of 7). Polluted waters are usually acid with a pH value of less than 7, while a lush river with much plant life is more alkaline.

Sea Salt

If an item is wetted with seawater and then allowed to dry, white salt crystals are left on the surface. These salts are highly deliquescent; they attract moisture from the air and make the surface damp even on a 'dry' day. This damp is highly concentrated salt solution and even more corrosive than seawater.

The effects of sea salt show themselves every day. Spray coming onto the deck is the most obvious way in which a boat gets covered with sea salt. The worst conditions are a strong wind (but not such a rough sea so as to wash the decks) in combination with hot sunshine, because the fine spray that comes aboard is rapidly dried by the sun. Sea salt can build up like this until there is a white crust over everything. 'Salt caked' is the novelist's pet expression.

There is only one way to remove salt crystals and that is with copious fresh water. Attempting to clean off a windscreen by wiping it with a rag merely results in smearing the salt. The crystals are sharp enough to scratch a Perspex window. Sea salt will remain clinging to a surface until washed off by rain or a fresh water hose.

Very fine sea spray – almost invisible – comes aboard continuously on a windy day. One can see it in bright sunlight and feel its effect for a long time afterwards; hair feels sticky and trousers damp. This fine spray is carried through open windows and hatchways and makes clothes and bedding feel damp. Even at sheltered moorings a boat can be inundated with sea salt during a gale because the wind picks up seawater from breaking wavelets and carries it along in a belt of damp sea air just above the water. With an onshore gale, salt can be detected in the air many miles inland.

Sea salt can pervade everywhere on a small boat, but what is so difficult is that the salt crystals deposited are forever causing condensation and at much lower humidities than one would normally expect. For instance if a camera is subjected to the fine mist mentioned earlier and then taken home and left in its case in an unheated room over the winter it will present a sorry sight in the spring. Little droplets of water will cover the camera and there will be spots of corrosion on metal parts. The internal mechanism may also be rusted because the humidity of the air inside the camera case will always be higher because of the damp-attracting properties of the salt. A bare steel item left in that same room but *not* wetted with sea salt would not attract condensation nor would it rust.

Corrosion Preventers

To be more realistic this heading should read 'corrosion reducers' or 'temporary protective substances'. There are hundreds of proprietary oils, greases, additives, etc that are claimed to reduce corrosion, mainly for steel and iron components. These can be classed as follows: paint or spray-on oils or greases or de-watering agents that cover the item with a film to prevent water reaching the metal; those that are put into the water to reduce its corrosive nature (as in an engine cooling system); those that reduce humidity, e.g. silica gel.

The first group are probably very familiar since there are dozens of varieties of aerosol sprays in chandlery and hardware shops and motoring shops. Perhaps the best known are the silicone sprays that are useful to chase damp off sparkplug leads etc in wet weather. They are also useful to protect aluminium and chrome,

SEAWATER AND SEA SALT

besides easing pulleys and locks etc. There are also compounds that
can be sprayed or brushed on that leave a hard film that can
subsequently be washed off with white spirit. Others form a soft
film. Grease intended for marine work should be resistant to water
and not washed off easily; such grease is useful for sterntubes,
rigging screws etc. (The large outboard manufacturers have a range
of sprays and greases as do the large oil companies.)

The trouble with all these types of coatings is that protection is
temporary rather than permanent. Also most of them are greasy to
the touch and not therefore very 'clean'. They collect dust and dirt,
and are not generally of use in very wet conditions or underwater
because they tend to get washed off. Knowing these limitations, it
can be seen that they are most useful for temporary protection of
parts under cover, for instance the engine. But even so, regular
renewal is necessary.

A traditional coating that is still widely used is anhydrous
lanolin. It is useful for rigging components and deck fittings.

Anticorrosion lubricating oils and greases are available for
special uses. For instance rather than leave ordinary oil in an engine
sump during the winter layup one can replace it with a 'preservative
engine oil' which also has a vapour rust-inhibitor to permeate all
through the block and head. Outboard gear oil is another special
oil that gives corrosion protection to the bare steel gears if a small
quantity of water leaks into the gearcase. To protect steel diesel
fuel tanks and injection pumps during layup there are special fuel
oils that also protect against corrosion. The engine is run on the
special oil to circulate it through the injection pump and injectors.

Rather than put a barrier on the metal's surface it is possible to
change the atmosphere around the metal so that corrosion is
stopped; of course this is only possible if the item is in an enclosed
space. A traditional method is to use silica gel to absorb the water
from the air; it can be dried out and re-used. Steel does not rust if
the relative humidity is less than 70–80% unless the surface has
traces of sea salt, in which case the relative humidity has to be
lowered to about 60%. Providing the enclosure is sealed, about 200
grams of silica per cubic metre of air space is effective (0.2 oz per
cu ft). 'Desiccator' plugs are one use on board a boat; they are put
in place of the sparkplugs during layup.

Another method is to put into the space a substance that

produces a vapour that inhibits corrosion. These are called 'vapour phase inhibitors' or 'volatile corrosion inhibitors'; they come in tablet form or in bags or as treated paper. Commonly used for packaging steel parts, probably the only use on board a boat is for the tool box and for protecting engine spares. VPIs can in some cases discolour plastics and attack copper.

Appendices

Strengths and Densities of Common Boat Metals

	lbs/cu. in.	Yield (or proof) stress (tons/sq. in.)	UTS tons/sq. in.
'Mild' steel	0.28	10–16	30
Cast iron	0.26	–	10–20
Cor-Ten A	0.26	22	31
Aluminium alloys	0.097	8	18–20
Copper sheet	0.32	4–6	14–16
70/30 Brass	0.31		20–30
60/40 Brass	0.31	8–12	20–30
Aluminium brass	0.31		21–35
Manganese bronze	0.30	14–16	28–32
Silicon bronze	0.31	7–9	17–23
Gunmetal, cast	0.29	8–12	13–20
Aluminium bronze	0.29	10–15	23–32
Nickel-aluminium-bronze	0.27	16–26	40–45
Stainless steel Type 304 sheet	0.29	15	38
Type 316 sheet	0.29	18	40
90/10 Copper-nickel, annealed	0.32	4–8	20
Monel 400, annealed	0.32	11–22	31–40
Monel K400, annealed	0.32	18–23	40–50
Lead	0.41	0.5	1

The strength values are only given as a rough guide because in most cases the strength of the metal is affected very much by the method of manufacture – hot and cold working, heat treatment, etc – quite apart from the exact composition.

UTS = ultimate tensile strength.
Castings are usually weaker than wrought products.
To convert density expressed as lbs/cu. in. to grams per cc, multiply by 27.7
To convert stress expressed as tons/sq. in. to N/mm^2 multiply by 15.4.

Proprietory Stainless Steel Propeller Shafts

An example of what is available commercially is provided by AQUAMET shafts. Four types of AQUAMET material are available: 17, 18, 19, and 22.

	Mn	Ni	Cr	Cu	Mo	Yield strength psi
17	1	3–5	14.5–16.5	3.5	–	105000
18	11–14	0.5–2.5	16.5–19	–	–	120000
19	2	8–10.5	18–20	–	–	130000
22	4–6	11.5–13.5	20.5–23.5	–	1.5–3	135000

Corrosion resistance increases with the type number and so does the cost!
AQUAMET 22 is claimed to be better than 316 stainless corrosion-wise, while AQUAMET 17 is similar to 304.

Weights and Measures

1 micron = 0.001 mm
1 mil = 1 'thou' = 0.001 in. = $25\mu m$ = 25 microns = 0.025 mm
1 metre = 3.28 ft.
1 in. = 25.4 mm

1 kg = 2.2 lbs
1 ton [force]/sq. in. = 15.4 Newton/mm^2 = 1.57 kg/mm^2 = 2240 lbs[force]/sq. in. (psi)

1 m/sec = 3.28 ft/sec
1 knot = 1.15 mph = 1.69 ft/sec
1 km/hour = 0.54 knot = 0.62 mph

Glossary

Acid-Alkaline   Related to the hydrogen ion activity in a liquid. Measured by pH value on a scale ranging from 0 to 14. A neutral solution is about 7; acid solutions have a lower pH, alkaline higher. The taste sense can detect acidity or alkalinity very well.

Alloy   A mixture of two or more elements, e.g. copper and zinc which form brass. The term 'light alloy' commonly refers to *aluminium* alloy.

Annealing   Heating a metal to within a certain temperature range in order to soften it and increase ductility.

Aluminizing   Hot-dipping or spraying steel components with aluminium.

Anode   The electrode of a cell at which positive electrical current passes into the electrolyte. Usually the anode material dissolves into the electrolyte, i.e. galvanically corrodes. The opposite electrode of the cell is called the *cathode*.

Anodizing   Conversion of the surface of a metal into oxide by a process of electrolysis to improve corrosion resistance. Aluminium is often anodized.

Antifouling Paint   A paint containing poison which prevents marine plant and animal growth for a limited period.

Barrier Coat   Or 'tie coat'. A paint which isolates one coat from another to prevent chemical interaction between them. Also to ensure good adhesion to an old coat.

Blast-Cleaning (Shot-Blasting, Grit Blasting)   A means of thoroughly cleaning steel. Sand, grit or iron shot is flung against the steel in a continuous stream. Best preparation for painting.

Cathodic Protection   A means of preventing underwater corrosion. The item to be protected is made the cathode of an electric cell either by an external electrical source or by coupling the item to a less noble metal. Sufficient current density will stop bare steel rusting in seawater.

Carbon Steels   Those containing not more than 0.5% Mn and 0.5% Si. All other steels are '*alloy steels*'.

Carvel   A technique for building wooden hulls in which the planks are butted up against each other, the seams being caulked and the outer surface smooth. *Clinker* or lapstrake hulls have the planks overlapping and do not require caulking.

Cast   Made by pouring molten metal into a mould and allowing it to cool. Metals suitable for casting are usually slightly different in composition from those intended for wrought products (sheet, plate, section). Thus cast iron is different from wrought iron, cast steel is different from steel plate (which is wrought), and cast aluminium from wrought aluminium.

Cavitation   In a fast flow of water the pressure can drop so low that cavities are formed. These cavities look like a stream of bubbles and where they collapse on a metal surface cavitation erosion takes place. Under high loads propellers and pumps can often cavitate, resulting in erosion, noise and vibration.

Chlorinated Rubber Paint   A pigmented solution of plasticized chlorinated rubber which forms a thick, tough, leathery coating.

Coal Tar Epoxide Paints   A mixture of coal tar and epoxide; a two-part paint ideal for steel hulls underwater.

Concentration Cell   A galvanic cell caused by differences in concentration of the electrolyte at the electrodes of the cell.

Corrosion Fatigue · Simultaneous fatigue and corrosion. Leads to cracking without any obvious corrosion.

Creep   Metals gradually deform under constant stress, depending on the temperature. Lead creeps at room temperature but stronger metals only creep at very high temperatures.

Crevice Corrosion   Localized attack in narrow crevices filled with water, caused by some slight difference in water quality such as oxygen content. An electric cell is thus set up. Crevices can be caused by bolted joints, for example. Stainless steel is prone to crevice corrosion.

Dehumidification   Deliberate decrease of the water content of air. If the level is reduced below a critical value corrosion can be stopped.

GLOSSARY

Deliquescence The property of absorbing moisture from the air and finally becoming liquid, e.g. sea salt.

Density Weight per unit of volume (cubic foot or cubic metre). *Specific gravity* is the density relative to fresh water where water equals 1, steel $7\frac{1}{2}$, lead 11, and so on.

Dezincification Loss of zinc in a copper-zinc alloy such as brass, leaving a porous and weak mass of red copper.

Ductile A metal is said to be ductile if it can be permanently drawn (stretched) appreciably.

Electrode Metal immersed in an electrolyte through which current can pass to or from the electrolyte. See *cathode* and *anode*.

Electrolysis Decomposition of an electrolyte by the passage of an electric current. Also loosely used to mean corrosion of the metals at the electrodes.

Electrolyte A liquid which can conduct electricity.

Erosion Corrosion or Impingement Attack Corrosion caused by a high-velocity stream of water acting on a metal. Any corrosion product is swept away exposing new metal that in turn corrodes.

Etch Primer (or Wash Primer) A paint usually containing phosphoric acid, which helps adhesion of the subsequent paint scheme to steel, aluminium and zinc.

Fatigue A continuous renewal of stress, leading to fatigue cracking. The stress may be much less than that needed to break the metal under a steady load.

Ferrous Describes an alloy containing the element iron (Fe).

Galvanic Corrosion An electric cell is set up by two electrodes of different metals immersed in an electrolyte and electrically coupled: one electrode corrodes, the other is protected.

Galvanizing Sometimes means 'coating with zinc'; sometimes refers only to 'hot-dip galvanizing'. Steel can also be coated with zinc by electroplating (electrogalvanizing), spraying or sherardizing.

Half-Cell One electrode in an electrolytic cell used as a reference for measuring the potential of other metals.

Hydrogen Embrittlement Metal embrittlement caused by the absorption of hydrogen. Usually only applies to very high-strength metals.

Ion An electrically charged atom or group of atoms. Ions enable a liquid to pass an electric current.

Inhibitor   A substance which when added to a corrosive liquid reduces its corrosiveness.

Light Alloy   Usually refers to an alloy of aluminium but can also mean an alloy of magnesium.

Malleable   A malleable metal is one which can be beaten or rolled into plates without cracking. A property which is very similar to ductility.

Microbiological Corrosion   Caused by micro-organisms, often anaerobic bacteria. Corrosion can proceed even if oxygen is absent, as in stagnant or oil-covered water or polluted mud.

Noble   Word used to denote a potential higher (more 'positive') in the galvanic series; the opposite is *base*.

Oleo-Resinous Paint   A paint consisting of drying oils and natural or synthetic resins.

Passivity   State of a metal surface after being deliberately polarized by being made the anode of a cell. In effect the metal is made more noble and less subject to corrosion. (Opposite: *activity*.) See *Anodizing*.

Patina   Long-term surface corrosion product, e.g. the greeny verdigris on copper and copper alloys.

Phosphating   Coating by chemical conversion, by means of a phosphate solution. Often applied to steel prior to painting.

Pitting   Localized attack resulting in pits often small in area but deep and self-perpetuating. Stainless steel is prone to pitting.

Plastic Deformation   When a metal is strained beyond its *elastic* limit it goes 'plastic' and does not return to its original shape. Any plastic deformation means that very high stresses were involved.

Polarize   To change the potential of an electrode by application of a current. Different metals polarize different amounts, hence affecting the current flow and therefore the corrosion rate.

Relative Humidity   A ratio (%) of the amount of water in a given volume of air to the amount required to saturate the air.

Sacrificial Anode   A piece of base metal deliberately coupled to the item to be protected. The anode gradually corrodes away while protecting the cathode.

Saponification   Decomposition by alkali, as results in conventional paint from cathodic protection.

Sealant   A thick sealing 'goo', used for bedding fittings onto a

213

deck etc. The sealant fills any gap and prevents the ingress of water. It partially sets but remains slightly flexible. There are many good brands available from yacht chandlers.

Season Cracking Cracking due to the combination of corrosion and stress. A term usually associated with brass.

Stray Current Electrical currents seeking an 'earth' or on a boat the seawater potential.

Stress Corrosion Combination of steady stress and corrosion, causing cracking without visible signs of corrosion. Often caused by locked-in stresses produced by forming, etc during manufacture.

Stress-Relieving Heating a casting or welded fabrication to reduce the locked-in stresses caused by solidification and cooling.

Two-Wire Electrical System Two insulated wires leading from electrical supply to and back from all electrical items, rather than using the engine or hull as an 'earth return'. Earth return systems are commonly used on cars to save on wiring cost.

Vapour Phase Inhibitor (VPI) An inhibitor which in a gaseous state is transferred to a metal surface to prevent corrosion. Works well only in a confined or air-tight space.

Weld Decay Corrosion and cracking of the heat-affected zone close to a weld. Applies to some stainless steels.

Working (Hot or Cold) A metal is 'worked' if it is taken beyond its yield point. Some can be cold-worked (to make the desired shape during construction); others have to be hot-worked, partly so that they do not crack and partly because the metal is softer at higher temperatures.

Wrought Worked into shape, either hot or cold, by sheer force.

Yield Point The highest strain beyond which a metal ceases to behave elastically. Up to its yield point the metal will return to its original size and shape when the load is released. The yield point of mild steel, for instance, is about half its breaking strength. Most other metals do not exhibit a well defined yield point, and a small arbitrary plastic extension is used and called *proof strength*.

Marine Materials

Carbon Steel Lower strength grades are often called mild steel. It is the basic cheap constructional metal used for ship and boat hulls, cars, bridges etc. Easily formed and welded with good strength properties, but it rusts.

Low-Alloy Steel Small additions of nickel and copper to mild steel enhance strength and slow the rate of rusting when left bare in the atmosphere.

High Strength Steels Small alloying additions and heat treatment give various types of steels which have very high strengths (up to ten times that of mild steel) and resistance to cracking. All types rust.

Cast Iron The basic cheap iron (e.g. 'grey' cast iron). Rusts as badly as carbon steel and has low tensile strength.

Nickel Cast Iron Addition of 1–3% nickel enhances strength. Rusts.

SG Iron 'Spheroidal graphite' iron. A modern shock-resistant iron as strong as cast steel but as castable as grey iron. Rusts.

Austenitic Cast Iron ('Ni-Resist') Addition of 13–36% nickel much reduces the rate of rusting. Strong yet castable.

Type 304 Stainless Steel (18/8 or EN58E) Tends to rust-stain unless kept clean. Pits deeply when immersed in seawater.

Type 316 Stainless Steel (18/10/3 or EN58J) The modern 'standard' stainless steel for marine work though it does have a tendency to pit when immersed in seawater.

Copper Soft, but good corrosion resistance except in fast-flowing water.

Brass A copper-zinc alloy. Many varieties but all prone to dezincification when used in seawater. 'Aluminium brass' is the best brass because it has the least amount of zinc. Common 60/40 brass is the worst. Brasses can be made less liable to dezincification by the addition of arsenic or tin.

Gunmetal (G Bronze) A zinc-free, very corrosion resistant alloy but not as strong as brass.

Aluminium Bronze Better alternative to brass. Reasonably strong and very corrosion resistant.

Nickel-Aluminium-Bronze (NAB) Better alternative to aluminium bronze.

Copper-Nickel Two types – 70/30 and 90/10 – both very corrosion resistant. 70/30 is stronger than 90/10. Excellent material for high-velocity seawater piping and heat exchanger tubing.

Silicon Bronze Strong and very corrosion resistant.

Manganese Bronze Actually a 60/40 brass, but stronger. Very prone to dezincification. Nevertheless a common material for propellers, shafts and deck fittings.

Alloy 400 (Monel) Very strong and corrosion resistant.

Nickel-Chromium Alloys New high-performance alloys, e.g. Alloy 825, Alloy 625 (trade names Incoloy, Inconel, et al).

Aluminium Only marine types, e.g. silicon and magnesium aluminium alloys, are corrosion resistant in seawater. Not very strong. High-strength aluminium-copper alloys corrode and stress-crack very rapidly in seawater.

Zinc A very weak metal. Widely used as a metal coating to protect steel: galvanized, sprayed, sherardized etc.

Titanium Strong and inert.

Bibliography

In the professional world of the corrosion engineer there is a vast range of technical literature. Consequently to list just a few titles is very difficult. There are virtually no 'non-technical' books that are digestible to the ordinary boat owner: hence this book. Marine corrosion is rarely mentioned in the yachting magazines (except perhaps *Practical Boat Owner*), which also contributes to the widespread ignorance on the subject.

Corrosion Resistance of Metal and their Alloys, Laque and Copson, Chapman & Hall Ltd, London

A Guide to the Selection of Marine Materials, Nickel Development Institute, The Holloway, Alverchurch, Birmingham

Corrosion Handbook, H. H. Uhlig, John Wiley, New York

Marine Corrosion, T. H. Rogers, Newnes, London

Recommended Practice for the Protection and Painting of Ships, BMT Wallsend Research Station, Wallsend, Tyne and Wear

British Navy Board Report to the Admiralty on the First Coppering Experiment – 1763, reprinted in America *Neptune* July 1941

Report on Stress Corrosion Cracking of Austenitic Chromium-Nickel Stainless Steels, American Society for Testing Materials, Special Technical Publication No. 264, March 1960

International Nickel booklets on many aspects of corrosion, Nickel Development Institute, The Holloway, Alverchurch, Birmingham

Metals Handbook, 8th Edition Vol. I, American Society for Metals, Ohio, USA. Voluminous technical handbook covering all metals and all environments.

Corrosion Resistance of the Austenitic Chromium-Nickel Stainless Steels in a Marine Environment, Nickel Development Institute, The Holloway, Alverchurch, Birmingham

BIBLIOGRAPHY

The Interrelation of Corrosion and Fouling of Metals in Seawater, INCO Europe Ltd

Aluminium Boat Building, 2nd Edn, Sims, Adlard Coles Nautical, London

Small Steel Craft, Ian Nicolson, Adlard Coles Nautical, London

Marine Radio Interference Suppression, Lucas-CAV Publication.

Timber Decay in Boats, HMSO

Corrosion and Corrosion Control, Uhlig, John Wiley, New York

The Stress Corrosion of Metals, H. L. Logan, John Wiley, New York

Corrosion Prevention Directory, HMSO. Lists consultants, suppliers, standards, books

Booklets by manufacturers of marine equipment, in particular those published by CAV Ltd on Electrical Interference and Electrical Systems

Electrical Installations for Wood Yachts, Lloyds Register of Yachts

Aluminium and the Sea, Pechiney Rhenalu, 10 Place des Vosges, 92048 Paris-la-Défense 5 Cedex 68, France

Seawater Corrosion Handbook, edited by M. Schumacher, Noyes Data Corporation, Park Ridge, New Jersey, USA

Some Addresses

In the UK

Aluminium Federation, Broadway House, Calthorpe Road, Birmingham B15 1TN. Trade Association.
Tel 0121 456 1103 Fax 0121 456 2274

British Steel Corrosion Advice Service, British Steel plc, Swinden Technology Centre, Moorgate, Rotherham S60 3AR
Tel 01709 820 166 Fax 01709 825 337

British Marine Industries Federation, Meadlake Place, Thorpe Lea Road, Egham, Surrey TW20 8HE. Trade association for marine industry.
Tel 01784 473 377 Fax 01784 439 678

British Standards Institution, 382 Chiswick High Road, London W4 4AL
Tel 0181 996 9000 Fax 0181 996 7400

Copper Development Association, Orchard House, Mutton Lane, Potters Bar, Herts EN6 3AP
Tel 01707 650 711 Fax 01707 642 769. Technical booklets.

M G Duff International Ltd, Unit 2 West, 68 Bognor Road, Chichester PO19 2NS. Specialists in cathodic protection.
Tel 01243 533336 Fax 01243 533422

Galvanised Bolts & Nuts Ltd, 115 Lodgefield Road, Halesowen, West Midlands B62 1AX
Tel 0121 602 3333 Fax 0121 602 3222

GKN plc, PO Box 55, Ipsley House, Ipsley Church Lane, Redditch, Worcs B98 0TL
Tel 01527 517 715 Fax 01527 517 700

International Paint Ltd, 24–30 Canute Road, Southampton SO14 3PB
Tel 01703 226 722 Fax 01703 661 532

SOME ADDRESSES

Institute of Corrosion, 4 Leck House, Lake Street, Leighton Buzzard LU7 8TQ.
Tel 01525 851 711 Fax 01525 376 696

Lloyd's Register of Shipping, 100 Leadenhall Street, London EC3A 3BP
Tel 0171 709 9166 Fax 0171 488 4796

National Corrosion Service, National Physical Laboratory, Teddington, Middlesex TW11 0LW
Tel 0181 977 3222 Fax 0181 943 6177. Government advisory Service.

Timber Research and Development Association, Stocking Lane, Hughenden Valley, High Wycombe, Bucks HP14 4ND
Tel 01494 563091 Fax 01494 565487

Wolfson Unit, University of Southampton, Southampton SO17 1BJ
Tel 01703 585 044 Fax 01703 671 532

In the USA

American Boat and Yacht Council, 3069 Solomon's Island Road, Edgewater, MD 21037
Tel (410) 956 1050 Fax (410) 956 2737

American Bureau of Shipping (ABS), 45 Eisenhower Drive Paramus NJ 07653–0910
Tel (201) 368 3961

American Iron and Steel Institute (AISI), 1101 17th Street NW, Suite 1300, Washington DC 20036
Tel (202) 452 7100 Fax (202) 463 6573

National Marine Manufacturers Association, 200 East Randolph Drive, Suite 5100, Chicago, IL 60601
Tel (312) 946 6200 Fax (312) 946 0388

The Society of Naval Architects and Marine Engineers, 601 Pavonia Avenue, Jersey City, NJ 07306
Tel (201) 789 4800 Fax (201) 798 4975

US Coast Guard Headquarters – Commandant, 2100 Second Street SW, Washington DC 20277–3057
Tel (800) 368 5647

Index

INDEX

INDEX